Mills & Boon
Best Seller Romance

A chance to read and collect some of the best-loved novels from Mills & Boon—the world's largest publisher of romantic fiction.

Every month, six titles by favourite Mills & Boon authors will be re-published in the *Best Seller Romance* series.

A list of other titles in the *Best Seller Romance* series can be found at the end of this book.

Violet Winspear

LOVE IN A STRANGER'S ARMS

MILLS & BOON LIMITED
LONDON · TORONTO

First published 1977
Australian copyright 1983
Philippine copyright 1977
This edition 1983

ISBN 0 263 74311 X

Set in Linotype Times 11 pt.
02–0538

Made and printed in Great Britain by
Richard Clay (The Chaucer Press) Ltd,
Bungay, Suffolk

CHAPTER ONE

THE big creamy camellias arrived first, and the girl in the hospital bed lay looking at them, vaguely aware of their exotic beauty and yet strangely incurious about who had sent them to her, or even brought them by hand.

The following day came the grapes, purple-black and lush, arranged on a dish with a ray of sunlight catching the bloom of their skins. Then sweets were delivered in a satin box tied by a deep blue bow, and by this time the girl was feeling less feeble and able to reach the tiny hand-printed label that was affixed to the bow. *San Devilla.* She shaped the words with her lips, but her mind was completely blank of any meaningful recollection of the name. Was it the name of a house? Was it her home, or did a friend live there? The kind-hearted person who sent her the flowers and fruit and expensive-looking sweets.

When a nurse came into the room she was invited to help herself to some of the sweets. 'The *señora* is too kind!' The young nurse eyed the array of delectable confectionery with a glint in her eyes. 'They seem almost too good to touch, but I fear I cannot resist.'

The patient lay in bed and watched the nurse, taking in her Latin eyes and the darkness of her hair under the small white cap. 'Where am I?' It was the first time she had asked that question. 'Who am I?'

'You are in hospital in Cordoba.' The nurse ate a pink candy with delicate greed and smiled at the pale face against the pillows.

'Cordoba . . .?'

'In the southern region of Spain. You don't remember, *señora*?'

'Not a solitary thing.' The girl raised her left hand but found it bare of a ring. 'Why do you call me *señora*? Am I—married?'

'Indeed! Take a look at your right hand.' Then as if the nurse felt that her patient still lacked the energy she came and lifted the slim hand from the sheet and sunlight speared through the louvres and there was a gleam of gold and a shimmer of blue gems. The girl stared at the rings and a frightened look came into her eyes and beneath the sheet her heart set up a sudden clamour of alarm that made her feel breathless. A pain shot through her head and she blinked against the burning shimmer, and had not the faintest idea that her eyes held terror and were as densely blue as the large sapphire, having a kind of luminosity to them. Her nose was slender and her lips were full. Her hair was braided down over the bedcovers and that thread of sunlight had woven itself into the strands of deep gold . . . golden as the *fleur-de-lys* on a battle banner. At present it was a pale and haunting face, with a certain beauty to it.

Her eyes seemed mesmerised by the wedding ring, then suddenly her lips twisted with pain and it was as if her clouded mind felt a stab of memory too harsh to endure. Her hand folded into a fist until the knuckles stood out whitely under the smooth skin.

'Why are the rings on my right hand?' She glanced at the nurse, and it didn't seem strange that she should be aware of the general facts of life while remaining unaware of those that were personal to her.

'Your husband is a Spaniard, *señora*. It is the custom of Spain.'

'I see.' The girl bit her lip. 'And . . . what nationality am I?'

'We were informed that you were from Boston in the United States.'

'I'm American! Do you happen to know my—my name?'

A certain pity sprang into the Latin eyes, for there was something so helpless in the way the girl asked to be acquainted with her own name. 'You are called Arabel. An attractive name, eh?'

'Arabel.' The girl spoke listlessly, for the quaint name opened no door that let in a rush of memory. 'And what is the—Spanish part?'

'You are the Señora Ildefonso de la Dura.' The nurse spoke with a definite note of awe in her voice.

Arabel absorbed the name but was quite unable to relate to it in any way at all. That note of awe had not been lost on her and her fingers clenched the bedcovers and it was all she could do to stop herself from crying out that it wasn't true . . . it wasn't possible that she was the wife of some unknown Spaniard. She felt as if she had been dropped into a strange dream from which she couldn't awake. Her very identity was wiped from her mind and soon, perhaps tomorrow, she was going to meet a man who might be as stern and grand as his name . . . a stranger who would come and claim her as his wife.

'I—I'm lost,' she whispered, and her gaze moved slowly around the clinical room. 'How did I come to be here—what happened to me? Have I been in an accident?'

'You are not to concern yourself with any of that, *señora*, not just at present. Now let me make your pillows more comfortable——'

'No!' Arabel drew away from the ministrations of her nurse. 'You're being evasive and I must know what has made me like this, unable to remember a simple thing like my own name, unable to recall a single detail of my—my husband's face. What is the matter with me?'

'Please, you must not get excited,' the nurse began to look worried. 'It isn't good for you and will set you back just as you have begun to make recovery——'

'From what?' Arabel's blue eyes were desperate. 'I must be told!'

'You have amnesia following a concussion of the head.' The nurse bit her lip. 'That is all I can tell you. The doctor will explain fully when you are ready to be told, but you must understand that you are still rather weak and you must rest your body and your mind and then you will make a full recovery.'

Arabel stared at the nurse and under the fine silk of her nightdress she could feel the pounding of her heart. 'If you won't tell me right this minute, then I demand that you bring the doctor to me. I have to know—I have to, nurse, or go crazy!'

'Very well,' the nurse looked a little distracted. 'I will see if Doctor Guardano is available. Lie quiet, *señora*, and allow that rapid pulse to quieten down before he comes.'

The door closed and Arabel was left alone, the sheet still gripped in her fingers, that thread of sunlight still playing in the great blue gem of the costly ring on her hand. So he was rich, this Spaniard to whom she belonged, this faceless figure who was lost to her in the clouded realms of her injured mind. He was able to afford a private room for her in this Spanish hospital, and he seemed to care enough to send her fruit, flowers and sweets.

She should have felt cared for and protected, but instead he evoked a twisting of the nerves in the very pit of her stomach. In her mind he was a blank . . . but her body seemed to know him, and to be apprehensive of him.

How come that she, an American, had married a Spaniard? She closed her eyes and tried to force some ray of recollection into her mind, but the veils wouldn't give, they wouldn't swing apart to reveal what lay hidden there. How had it happened that she had concussion . . . wasn't that caused by a blow on the head? Strange and somehow frustrating that she should be aware of generalities and yet shut off from any personal knowledge of herself and the man whose rings she wore.

What meaning could that have . . . that there might be things in her life that she didn't wish to remember?

She was half-dozing when the door of her room opened and admitted this time a sleek, dark-haired man clad in a white coat. He came to the bedside and she watched him as he took her by the hand and held her wrist in his lean fingers. His eyes were fixed upon her face and she saw a slight frown contract his dark brows.

'You have been getting worked up, eh?' He shook his head at her. 'It does you no good and will only make you feel tired.'

'It does me no good to be kept in the dark about my—my accident,' she replied. 'I'm ready to be told, and I'm not a child, if those rings on my hand are any indication of my status.'

'The problem is,' he sat down carefully on the side of her bed and moved a pair of shrewd eyes over her face, 'that in your case I cannot say that you have been in an accident—not the regular sort which involves a vehicle or a piece of household equipment. You follow me?'

'You mean—someone struck me on the head?'

'Ah, so you are a bright young woman! I supposed it from the very start—American women are well educated and they have active, curious minds. Yes, unfortunately you were struck on the head, and the result was a concussion which has left you—but only temporarily—dispossessed of your memory. Not a very comfortable state of mind, but one that will resolve itself—given time, and given your co-operation. You must not force the mind to respond to your will, *señora*. The mind is a most delicate organ.'

'Who struck me on the head?' Her voice was quiet and tense. 'Tell me that at least.'

'I would have preferred the *señor hidalgo* to explain matters.'

'Who?' Her eyes widened and seemed to cast blue shadows over the finely boned contours of her face.

'Your husband, *señora*.' A look of compassion came and went in the doctor's eyes. 'You still have no recollection of him?'

'None at all.' She shivered. 'When you mention him you might as well be speaking of a stranger. It's rather awful—like being cut loose in space!'

'An apt description.' Dr Guardano patted her hand. 'You owe him your life, even if you are unable to recall the circumstances.'

'My life!' Arabel felt again that contraction of nerves deep inside her. 'What heroic thing did he do?'

The doctor's frown returned and he looked worried by her nervous fear of the one person in all the world whom she should be eager to remember. Instead she seemed to shrink from the faintest memory of him.

'This much I can tell you, *señora*. You were arrested in Venezuela for harbouring a pair of students who were responsible for arson at a large oil refinery—a rebellious action on their part, carried out against those in authority. You gave them refuge in your apartment, but a neighbour became curious upon hearing sounds while you were out at work as secretary to a company executive. Your apartment was raided, the pair of rebels were discovered, and you were picked up by the police. It seems there was a scuffle, that you attempted to escape them and were knocked down. Word of your arrest reached the Señor Ildefonso de la Dura by way of the man for whom you worked. Strings were pulled in order to secure your release, otherwise you would now be languishing in a cell, unaware of your own identity and left to your fate. Prudent men don't get involved in political situations, but the *señor hidalgo* dared to do so on your behalf . . . he married you and brought you out of Venezuela as his wife.'

Arabel had listened intently to every word of the doctor's recital, but none of it made any sense to her. Latin rebels, brutal policemen, the coming to her rescue of a Spanish stranger ... what had she to do with any of this? Only the rather grim look on the doctor's face told her that he related facts and not an elaborate fiction.

'But I—I don't remember this man, and it certainly seems strange that he should lumber himself with someone who had been crazy enough to get mixed up with a pair of fire-raisers.' Arabel's eyes were filled with bewilderment. 'It makes no reasonable sort of sense—does it, doctor?'

'Not on the face of it,' he agreed. 'And at the present time you are still in a state of delayed shock and mental confusion. Later on when you remember the details——'

'But why is the *señor*'s face such a blank? If he married me after the blow was struck, he at least should be there in my mind even if the things that occurred beforehand are—missing.'

'Your actual collapse from the concussion took place on the air flight to Spain,' the doctor explained. 'You were brought to us in an ambulance from the airport, at which time you were quite unconscious and remained so for several hours. When you came out of it we kept you on drugs to keep you composed and that is why you have drifted in a kind of gentle limbo. I would have preferred that you remain tranquil a while longer, but it would seem that your curiosity is now wide awake even if——' He shrugged in a very Latin way. 'The memory will return, in time.'

'In time!' she echoed. 'A week, a month—a year? I can't recall a thing about my past life, and certainly not about Venezuela and why I was working there.'

'Possibly because it was a well-paid job.' Dr Guardano smiled a little. 'American women are not stay-at-home, are they? They like to see the world, and you were no exception. It was possibly foolish of you to get involved with these students, but on the other hand you are now the wife of an eminent man.'

'How—eminent is he?' Arabel felt her heart sink. 'Is he very old and creaky?'

The doctor stared at her a moment, and then he gave an amused laugh. 'The Señor Ildefonso de la Dura is far from being an elderly gentleman, *señora*. I think that he came to your rescue in prison is an indication that he was acquainted with you beforehand, and let me add that you are hardly a young woman who would go unnoticed in a Latin country, not with your very fair colouring.'

'Am I fair?' She looked at him for a moment, and then her fingers found her braid and she studied it. 'I see—oh God, it's awful to be like this, cut off from myself and from any recollection of the family I must have in America. Why didn't they help me—why did it have to be a stranger?'

'You must not torment yourself with all this mental probing, for the more you try the more like slippery eels will the memories slip away.' The doctor picked up a hand mirror from the locker and handed it to her. 'Look well at your own face, *señora*. I don't think you will be displeased.'

Arabel accepted the mirror and slowly raised it until her hair and features were reflected in the glass. Dark blue eyes that asked a hundred questions, lips with a tiny nerve flickering at the edge of them, high cheekbones with little hollows beneath them. An intriguing face, and it belonged to her . . . a face which had attracted a strange Spaniard . . . a man whom the doctor suggested she had known before the trauma of being hustled off to prison and suffering a blow which had on that forgotten flight suddenly blacked out her memory.

A sudden awful fatigue swept over her and as if sensing this the doctor took the mirror and made her lie down. 'I will send in the nurse with a sedative,' he murmured. 'Let me assure you that sleep is the best medicine for you.'

'For in that sleep, what dreams may come . . .'

'I beg your pardon, *señora*?' He looked perplexed.

'I believe I was quoting from something,' she said. 'Is that a good sign, do you think? Will I wake up and find that the cloudy veils have lifted?'

'You may well do so, *señora*, but don't pin too many hopes on a sudden filling up of the dam of memory. Each compartment of the mind must fill slowly, for the sake of your sanity.'

'I'm not crazy, am I?'

'Heaven forbid!'

She smiled slightly. 'You're kind, doctor—is he, I wonder?'

'A Spaniard with a young wife is invariably kind, *señora*.'

Comforting words, but were they necessarily true? It was the task of a doctor to be reassuring, but she was a wife who couldn't even remember her own bridal, and as a lonely sense of being cut off from family and friends swept over her, she was only too willing to accept the medication which the doctor had ordered for her. In a very short while things grew muzzy and she floated off into a dreamless sleep, her right hand flung out across the covers so the sapphire winked and gleamed whenever the sunlight touched the gem.

The following day she was carefully bathed by the nurse, dressed in a fresh silk nightdress, and had her hair brushed and loosened about her shoulders. The pillows were carefully banked behind her, and Arabel knew without asking that someone was coming to see her.

'There.' The nurse stood smiling at her. 'You look so young, like a small girl who has been very good and now is to be rewarded.'

'You mean my reward is a visitor, don't you?' Arabel wondered that she could speak so calmly when those tiny nerves were curling and twisting with a life of their own, there in the pit of her stomach. She almost wanted to groan, to beg that they didn't leave her alone with this strange man who claimed that she was his wife. It was some kind of a plot. If you had a husband and if you loved him, then you didn't shut him out of your mind as totally as this.

Her eyes moved sideways and dwelt on the beautiful pink carnations which had been delivered about an hour ago. At the base of the vase lay a package which she had not yet opened.

'Shall I unwrap your present?' asked the nurse. 'I am sure you are eager to see what your husband has sent you.'

'Not particularly.' The cool note in Arabel's voice was not assumed. She felt nothing but apprehension with regard to this man . . . her only certainty in all the world was that she had some very personal reason for feeling resentful that he laid claim to her and that others who might care for her seemed unaware of her presence here in Spain . . . as if he had deliberately kept it from them that she was in hospital suffering from amnesia.

All the flowers had come from him, and the gifts. When she had asked if there had been any telephone calls from anyone inquiring about her, they had said no, and had seemed to take it for granted that the only person concerned for her was this unknown Spaniard who called himself her husband.

'Come, allow me to open your gift, or your husband will assume that you aren't grateful for his kindness.'

'I'm certainly not grateful for the way he has left my family and friends in total ignorance of where I am,' Arabel replied stiffly. 'I daresay the flowers and the presents are to ease his conscience.'

An expression of shock flashed in the nurse's eyes, followed by a look of exasperation. 'Be assured that your husband is a gentleman. He is *muy distinguido*, and would do nothing that was not honourable.'

'I don't doubt that he's adept at clicking his heels and paying out flowery compliments,' Arabel rejoined. 'But I must have relatives in America and he seems not to have informed them of my whereabouts. Do Spanish husbands usually behave in such a high-handed manner, as if a girl no longer has a family of her own when she marries a lordly Latin?'

'There is every possibility, *señora*, that you have no one in America whom he could inform. It seems unfair to judge him, especially as your state of mind is so confused.'

Arabel bit her lip. It could be true what the nurse said, but if it was then it increased her sense of loneliness without easing the ache of wanting to avoid the man . . . this husband who was unavoidable because she was more or less a prisoner in a hospital bed, still rather physically weak, and with a mind that was not functioning normally.

She felt a flicker of temper that she was so . . . so at the mercy of these Spanish people who were kind enough but who seemed to be in awe of the Señor Ildefonso de la Dura.

'Oh, all right,' she muttered. 'Open the package if you must.'

The nurse smiled and did so, and caught her breath in admiration. In a case of delicate tortoiseshell lay a jewelled comb, the kind that Latin girls fixed in their hair, and there was also a white lace fan delicately painted with a spray of golden flowers. Both items were incredibly pretty, but Arabel clenched her hands and contained her impulse to touch them.

'Are they not delightful?' The nurse flicked open the fan and with an expert movement of her wrist she fluttered it and carried it to her face, hiding all but her sparkling Latin eyes.

'You may have it,' Arabel said. 'For being kind to me.'

'Oh no!' The girl quickly closed the fan and replaced it in the case. 'It is a gift from your husband and he would be furious if you gave it away. It is probably a family heirloom and you must treasure it.'

'But you are a Latin girl and it suits you. I'd like you to have the fan, and the comb if you like.'

'No.' The nurse backed away from the bed, and a perplexed look had come into her dark eyes, as if never before had she come across someone like Arabel, who treated costly and charming gifts from her husband as if they meant absolutely nothing to her. 'I will leave you now, *señora*, to go about my other duties. Is there anything you require before I go?'

'What about my clothes and my handbag?' Arabel smiled ironically. 'I'd like nothing better than to get out of here right now—before he arrives and the net closes a little more about me. I—I'm like a half-dazed moth, can't you see that? I struggle, but all you do is to help that man make a complete prisoner of me.'

The nurse gave a little shake of her head, as if to say to herself that the Americana was *loca*, poor thing, and had to be pacified. 'Eat some of your grapes, *señora*. In a short while the *señor hidalgo* will be with you and all will be well—you will see.'

The door closed behind her and Arabel clenched her teeth, as if to hear him referred to in that grand manner put her teeth on edge. She gazed at the fan and the comb ... charming, Latin, like everything else around her. There was no sign of anything that might be entirely hers, for even her nightdress had insets of intricate Spanish lace in the silk. She sighed and felt trapped, aware that there was nothing she could do but await this stranger who called himself her husband. Perhaps seeing him would clear the confusion from her mind, but would it release her heart from the terror that seemed to grip it?

Oh, why did terror have a hold on her heart when according to her doctor she had every reason to feel grateful to the *señor hidalgo*? He had come to her rescue and had used his influence to get her out of the clutches of the political police ... but how ... how on earth had she come to be mixed up with such people in the first place?

Was it all an elaborate lie, fabricated by this Spaniard who was coming here in a short while to lay claim to her? Yet why should he lie? What reason could he possibly have? The rings on her fingers were all too real; they fitted her finger, and the sapphire matched her eyes. She had to believe that she was the Señora Ildefonso de la Dura, even though she felt but a confused girl who possessed none of the knowledge of a married woman.

What had the doctor said . . . that the *señor* had married her in order to get her out of Venezuela? Could that possibly mean that she was a wife in name only and that even yet she might be free to return to America as soon as she was well enough to travel?

Some of the tension seemed to relax its hold on her. Oh yes, that had to be why Señor Ildefonso de la Dura was coming to see her. He was going to explain that their marriage had been but an expediency; a means to an end. Now that she was safe from retribution and couldn't be punished for helping those students, she would be set free altogether. Her lips trembled into a smile, but it was a smile that lingered for only a brief moment, dying away even as sunlight found the facets of the sapphire ring and set the stone glowing alight.

It sparkled, gleamed, shone, almost mockingly, and Arabel wasn't so confused in her mind that she could make herself believe that the gem was a fake . . . as false as the marriage vows which she couldn't even remember making.

CHAPTER TWO

THE little clock ticked on the bedside cabinet and the brightness of the sun against the white walls of the room was an indication that outside in the busy world the day was a warm one. In fact Spain was a hot country, wasn't it? While here in the hospital a cool atmosphere was maintained so that from where Arabel lay in bed she could feel a soft draught of air from a grille in the wall.

Upon the wall that faced the foot of her bed there was attached a carved crucifix, and suddenly she closed her eyes very tightly and breathed a prayer that might not be answerable in this Catholic country that clung tenaciously to all the old rules regarding marriage.

When she opened her eyes the door of her room was also standing open and a man was framed there, as in the oval shape of a large portrait. Arabel's eyes were fixed upon him and she thought how dark he looked against the white decor of the room; even his suit was darkly severe and perfectly cut to his lean figure. His shirt-front was flawlessly white against his swarthiness, and he might have been Tarik standing there, the one-eyed avenger of Florinda.

Even as Arabel stared at the black velvet patch over his left eye he raised a hand to it and a brief smile twisted his lips. 'Don't let this worry you, *mi vida*. Don't you remember it?'

His voice was deep, foreign, and Arabel could feel the torment of her nerves as she met his undamaged eye and found it carved at an angle in his face, with a strange ring of gold around the densely dark pupil. The strong bones of his face could be seen in hard detail under his skin, and his brows seemed like black slashes above the good eye and the patch that should certainly have rung a bell in her mind.

Surely she would not forget a detail so significant about the man who had married her?

Her eyes raced up and down his figure. He wasn't overpoweringly tall, but he was lithely built and firmly muscled, giving off an aura of supple, vigorous control over his every sinew . . . abruptly he closed the door behind him and Arabel could feel her instinctive recoil against the pillows behind her as he crossed the room towards her bed, walking with a litheness of movement almost feline, as if his bones and sinews responded to some deep inner rhythm of his native land. He leaned over her and lifted her right hand to his lips . . . she felt them warm and firm against her skin . . . alive and strange.

'You lie there with a face white like milk.' His voice and Latin accent tinged his words with several shades of meaning. 'The sun will be your remedy; it will stir honey into the cream.'

Her fingers moved in his and she wanted to pull away from him, for close like this he stirred no intimate memories, but only aroused in her a feeling of almost helpless terror. The lines beside his eye and lips were deeply incised in his swarthy skin, as if he lived a great deal in the sun and was also a man of responsibilities. She judged him to be in his late thirties, whereas she had only to look into the hand mirror to see that she was in her early twenties.

No immature boy, this man who held and warned her with his strong fingers that he was everything he claimed to be . . . her eyes fixed themselves upon his lips, which like everything else about him were firm and purposeful, and also with a promise of strong male passions in the hard curve of that lower lip.

'You look at me as if I frighten you,' he said. 'My touch, my face, are they so strange to you, Arabel?'

She gave a little shiver when he used her name . . . everything about him was more than strange. No handsome, charming Latin came to claim her for his own . . . this man sprang from the hot sun, the harsh soil, the deep secret heart of Spain. She knew that about him even as she looked at him with no other sort of recollection.

Again he touched a finger to his blind eye. 'A horn wound received at Talavera, and best covered up, for it isn't pretty. I was an *espada*, and you knew it when you married me. I am Don Cortez, and I do assure you, despite the bewilderment in your eyes, that I am your husband and in a day or so I shall be taking you home with me, to San Devilla.'

His words sank like barbs into her mind . . . this one-eyed stranger, this man who had been a matador, he was the master of San Devilla who sent her camellias and costly gifts of tortoiseshell and silk; who looked at her with the smouldering gaze of his ancestry.

'Is your house in the deep south?' she asked.

'Mi casa es tu casa,' he murmured. 'The *estancia* lies in the heart of Andalusia and like my wife it has a white, proud beauty.'

Arabel's heart seemed to beat in her throat when he said that, and she seemed to see what lay in his soul; a dash of the conquistador, a whisper of the Moor, a thread of pagan tenacity: all the things that made a *corrida de toros*, but surely not the husband of an American girl who had somehow fallen into his hands because of a crazy impulse which had led her to shelter a pair of hot-headed students.

'We can have our marriage annulled,' she said, with a touch of desperation in her voice; a hint of wild appeal in her blue eyes. 'It has served its purpose, for which I'm deeply grateful, Don Cortez.'

'Our marriage was performed by a Catholic priest, *mi vida.*' He gazed down at her; even like this, struck low and with a mind quite blank of any memory of him, she was a distractingly lovely girl. Her mouth against her pallor was soft and full in its pleading . . . made for the hard kisses of a man. 'For me, Arabel, every aspect of that sacrament happens to be binding.'

'But we aren't man and wife,' she cried out, 'not in the real sense of the words.'

'How can you know that?' he drawled. 'You have no recollection of me or of what I have been to you. Your mind is lost in a mist and my hand must guide you home.'

'The doctor told me why you married me,' she said, and now she was sitting forward and there was about her the intensity of a prisoner in the dock, who pleaded for her freedom of a judge with a hard, dark face, eagle-eyed and with a jaw like iron. 'He said you did it to—to save me from a prison sentence—that was most gallant of you, but now I'm begging you to understand that I don't know you, and that what I most want is to go home to my people in America. You must let them know where I am. You must!'

'But there is no one to inform, Arabel.' He looked directly down at her, an oddly menacing effect. 'You have no one but me. I am your protector, guardian and husband, and I intend to fulfil all my obligations . . . as you will fulfil yours.'

'You mean,' her pallor seemed to intensify, as did the deep blue of her eyes, 'I'm to stay married to you? That I'm to be your wife—against my will?'

'You are my wife.' His tone of voice was inexorable, and she was given some glimpse of what this man must have been like clad in the *traje de luces*, the matador's suit of lights—a grim harlequin of purpose, swinging the great cloak in defiance of the bull—and she—she was but a girl with a lost memory. 'You are mine, whether willingly or not, Arabel. It is a fact of life and you must face it.'

'I don't love you——'

'How can you know? Your memory has deserted you, so how can you be sure how it was between us before you lost all recollection of your time in Venezuela?'

'Are you saying I loved *you*? Oh no, I wouldn't forget a thing like love! I—I might forget what was painful to me, but surely I'd remember what had made me happy.'

'Amnesia, as the medico will explain to you, is no respecter of happy memories or sad ones. It comes down over the mind like a fog over a city and everything is blanked out, not just the back alleyways and shadowy recesses. The sun is lost, direction is difficult, and the wise woman follows the lamp of a friend.'

'Are you that, *señor*?' Her eyes met his with a sudden candour that was almost childlike, as if she knew already that she was going to have to trust him because there was no one else.

'Only time will tell you what I am, *mi esposa*,' he replied.

'So I must take a blind chance and follow you?'

'Yes. I am a Latin and inflexible when it comes to the woman whom the law calls my rib and right-hand piece.'

'You do realise, Don Cortez, that I've not been reared to the idea of marriage with a stranger.'

'Arabel, we all marry strangers. It is the living together that blends the man and woman, as the flour and fruit in the wedding cake.'

'So you are going to insist that I come home with

you—like this? In the dark about my past life, someone who had to ask strangers her own name? Will it really suit you, Don Cortez, to have a wife who feels nothing but apprehension about the future?'

'It is natural for you to feel that way.' He picked up the jewelled comb which he had sent her and held it so the sunlight caught in the gems. 'This will look charming in your hair. You like it, no?'

'It's very pretty.' She spoke tonelessly. 'Are you going to try and turn me into a Latin woman? You will have quite a task on your hands, *señor*, for even with a confused mind I am aware that it isn't in my nature to bow down to the so-called superior male of the species. Is it the truth, that I have no family who could be informed of my plight?'

'Your plight?' He raised quizzically a dense black brow, a scimitar of irony above that brilliant, eagle-like eye. 'You are safe enough in my hands, *niña*, and if it will make you feel more trusting of me, then permit me to show you our marriage certificate.'

He replaced the comb in the tortoiseshell case and took from an inner pocket of his well-cut jacket his dark leather wallet. He flipped it open and extracted a folded paper and handed it to her. 'You may, despite your loss of memory, be able to read our marriage certificate even though it is written in Spanish. I might inform you that you speak my language excellently and worked in Venezuela for a countryman of mine.'

Arabel could feel the tremor in her hands as she unfolded the paper and stared at it; for only a few moments was she baffled by the words, and then all at once she found herself reading them . . . it was totally true what he said, she could read Spanish, and she was officially the wife of Don Cortez Ildefonso de la Dura, native of Andalusia in the country of Spain.

Her full name was Arabel Marsha Ildefonso de la Dura y Lennox, citizen of the United States of America, and aged twenty-two. The man to whom she was married was thirty-nine, occupation landowner at his residence of San Devilla.

'All clear and above board,' he murmured. 'As you see, *mi esposa*.'

My wife! He kept on calling her that, and he had every right, but the realisation was terrifying that in a day or so she would travel to San Devilla where he would teach her to be his real wife.

As Arabel handed him back the official declaration of their marriage she felt as if she were handing herself to him and could do nothing to prevent the processes of law, and fate.

'None of this is real to me,' she said, pressing a hand to her brow as if to force the gates to yield; those iron gates of the mind behind which all memories of this man were securely locked away. So she had been Arabel Lennox working for a Spaniard known to Don Cortez . . . was that how they had met? Presumably it was . . . but she would never believe, never, that she and this ruthless-faced man had ever been in love. He just didn't seem to be the kind of man she could have cared for, even have liked. A man who fought bulls in the arenas of Spain, who had faced their awful fury and plunged a sword into their necks so that the red blood dyed the sands at his feet. It was barbaric! It was tormenting that she could remember such cruel things and yet forget so completely what lay closest to her heart.

'How did we meet?' she cried at him.

'We met,' he said, and leaning over her he touched a finger to her mouth. 'These lips my sacramental wine,' he murmured. 'At least they drank it, and made certain vows that not even the blade of an *espada* might sever.'

She stared into his face as if seeing it in a Latin mural. A smile played in his eye . . . dominant, letting her know he was her master.

'This doesn't feel like a marriage,' she said. 'It feels more like an abduction!'

'Nonetheless,' he drawled. 'Do you know that when a woman opposes the will of a man she is the cloak provoking the bull?'

'You are more like an eagle than a bull, Don Cortez.' She sat there tensely, forcing herself not to pull away from him, sensing that he could be as furiously provoked as any of the high-strung animals he had fought and killed. 'Was it gallantry on your part, marrying me, or the challenge you learned in the arena?'

'A little of both, *mi vida*. Even so, whatever the inducement, you are wedded to a Spaniard and his laws are the ones in force in this country, and with regard to marriage they are less flexible, shall I say, than in your own country. I trust, *querida*, that I make myself perfectly clear?'

'I am in no confusion about what you make clear,' she rejoined. '*A sus ordenes, señor*. As you ordain.'

As she spoke she watched the proud contraction of his nostrils, and saw again that a certain ferocity seemed to smoulder beneath his suavity. He had about him the forceful air of a man who knew exactly what he wanted . . . he wanted her and his Spanish laws had given him every right to her.

'So you are a landowner, *señor*.'

'*Ay*, a breeder of bloodstock to whom foreigners send their mares to be served. My young bulls are sold to farmers, if you were wondering if I bred for the bullrings.'

'I was,' she admitted. 'Surely in your case that would be the logical thing to do?'

'It could be, *querida*, that I am not a man who always does the logical thing.' A sardonic smile edged his lips. 'In the ring I became known as El Tuerto, but I am going to insist that my wife calls me by my given name.'

'The one-eyed,' she murmured. 'Were you using your blind eye when you married me, *señor*? I am sure if I ever felt any sort of love for you, then I'd feel it now. One loves with the heart, not with the mind.'

'*Ay*, and don't forget the body.' The look he gave her held the essence of challenge, as if in all his years as a matador he had never before taken on the taming of a woman. No, she told herself. As a daring *espada* he would have had the women at his feet; they would have thrown him their carnations and their affections and he would have casually picked them up and enjoyed them until their interest faded. But this time he had been intrigued enough to marry, and instead of choosing a raven-haired beauty of Andalusia he had chosen someone who was opposite to such women in every way.

'We say in Spain that a rich man is a better catch than a nice man,' he said drily. 'And I might as well tell you now that I earned the bulk of my money by the use of the cape and the sword.'

'It's a cruel sport.' She shuddered and was sure she saw again the cruelty in his face . . . what was a woman to a man who had given the *coup de grâce* to a courageous fighting bull? Many bulls, if by such a career he had made his fortune!

'For better or worse a couple have to learn about each other after their marriage,' he said.

'It's turn of the century!'

'It's far older than that, *mi vida.* It goes back to the time of the Moorish occupation, when the far south of Spain was overrun by them and they penetrated into every aspect of the life, and even to this day the land, the people, the very scents and shadows are almost of the Orient.'

'And that is where I must go and live—with a stranger?' Arabel spoke in an almost inaudible voice and he leaned nearer to her, until she breathed the tiger balm on his skin and the tang of cheroot smoke; until she actually felt the warmth and vigour of his hard-muscled body. She shrank away from him. This time she couldn't control the impulse.

His look, then, became piercing enough to cut her into ribbons, and the clinical whiteness of her room gave him the look of a man whose ancestors had come riding fast on Arab horses out of the burning desert, to make their courts and seraglios in the sunlight of Spain.

'I know that your nerves have been shot to pieces,' he said. 'I know that it is hard for you to take, that a seeming stranger should come to you and declare himself your husband. But as the poppy grows upon the field of battle so will the memories return—given time and the warm healing touch of the sun.'

'Don't you fear, Don Cortez, that the return of my memory might reveal that I have reason for hating you rather than loving you?' Again it was disturbing and menacing to be looked upon by a man whose left eye was completely covered by a patch of black velvet, and whose right eye had the penetration of an eagle swooping down on its prey. In any circumstances he would have been a formidable opponent, but he was by law the most intimate person in her life . . . believe it or not he was her husband.

'I learned as a young *torero* to kick fear into the

sand, for fear is like the cape to the bull, it provokes the forces of fate. An *espada* learns soon enough that he has a twin, his shadow and likeness by the name of Death, but if he's a wise man he ignores that silent shadow and goes directly for his target . . . the heart of the bull.'

A smile touched the hard lips that held the passion of the south. 'Do you suppose it is so much harder for a man to reach the heart of a woman?'

'Not my heart,' she rejoined. 'You're taking advantage of me, forcing your will upon mine because I'm hurt and lost in a strange country. You inform me I have no family, but why should I believe you? I'm sure that no man could be a matador without being utterly ruthless.'

'Quite true,' he agreed. 'He would very soon be trampled and gored if he didn't watch out for himself and be as cunning as the bull. But if I were out to deceive you, *guapa*, would I have told you that I was once so active in the arena? Would you have been any wiser, at this stage? Would you not have concluded that I was just a man of business?'

Arabel studied his face and sensed that any conclusions about him would have been that he had a forceful and unusual personality and was a man to beware of. Never in a foolish moment would she have taken it for granted that he was an ordinary sort of person.

'Then you swear it's the truth, Don Cortez, that I have no one in America to whom I can appeal?'

'I never swear, but I have been known to curse,' he replied. 'You are my wife, Arabel. You are under my protection.'

His wife; yet try as she might Arabel couldn't recall a single moment of their wedding ceremony, which must have been performed at the prison where she had been taken. A Spanish ceremony with a Latin priest to intone the vows, with grim men in uniform standing by as she was handed over to the custody of Don Cortez. The pulse that beat at the base of her throat felt like a tiny hammer . . . beating into fragments any hope she had harboured that such a marriage might be annulled.

She felt the penetration of his gaze, a black and gold talon raking over her skin. Then as if reading her thoughts he touched one by one the rings on her right hand. 'This is the gold ring of alliance, and in place of the traditional pieces of silver I gave you this band of platinum set with a sapphire. A deep and glowing sapphire that reflects the colour of your eyes.'

He spoke like a lover, she thought wildly, and as she shrank again from his closeness and the intimacy of his words she saw the half-closing of his eye that seemed to indicate a threat . . . a warning that he meant to be her lover in more than words. He had lived by action and had taken on more dangerous opponents than a mere woman, and the very set of his features told her that it was useless to appeal to him, for he wasn't the sort to be swayed by pity when for many years he had strode pitiless and arrogant into the hot arena with its sand-covered pavement.

Why should he pity her? To his Spanish reasoning, his matador judgment, his deep-rooted instincts, she was fortunate to be out of the clutches of the Venezuelan police and safely married to a man of means and property.

He had stepped in and rescued her and in the ageless tradition she must repay him with her body.

It was there in his single brilliant eye what he demanded of her, and there was no debating the fact that she would sooner be at his mercy than that of the warders of a grim prison house. Heaven help her, what crazy sort of impulse had led her to become involved with a pair of rebellious students! What had they been to her? Friends . . . or strangers who had burst in and demanded that she hide them?

It was all such a confusion and her mind seemed to be whirling like a leaf in a high wind.

'Whatever made me do such a thing?' she groaned.

He gave a brief, hard-lipped smile. 'It is all very well for a woman to be *emancipada*, but not always in a Latin country.'

'A woman's place is in the home, I suppose? She must care only about her kitchen and her husband's wants?'

'At least in doing so she saves herself from a battering that leads to a loss of memory. Spanish husbands might be taskmasters, but they don't beat their wives.'

'Not even unwilling ones, Don Cortez?' And the instant she spoke Arabel had the strangest feeling that she and this man were proceeding with some kind of private duel. She felt a stab of recognition in defying him, a sensation of delight when he gritted his teeth, as if for a moment she had got under his tough skin.

'Having dealt successfully with bulls I don't anticipate too much trouble in dealing with you, *mi vida*,' he drawled.

'What do you plan to use on me, El Tuerto, the *banderillas*? Those nasty little barbed sticks that make the poor beast even more tormented than that damn great cloak waving in its eyes and confusing it?'

'Ah, so you have not forgotten the *corrida*?' He leaned close and there was an intent look on his brown face. 'That you do recall even if you don't remember me?'

'Yes——' Arabel bit her lip. 'It's strange, but I do

recall the impersonal and yet there's a frustrating veil over everything else, the things I want more than anything to remember. I—I must have attended a bullfight and I must have hated it like hell!'

'Romantic women do hate it,' he said, in almost a grave tone of voice. 'By romantic I probably mean sensitive, and inclined to be carried away by ideals. The Latin woman is more fundamental, more down to earth, more in tune with herself as a woman. Your sort is a little too concerned with the knightly deed and the holy grail . . . it probably comes from being brought up in an orphanage which had a library of old-fashioned books. You read far too much as a child and grew up expecting men to be like those fictional heroes who dared all and demanded very little——'

'The orphanage?' She clutched at his sleeve, touching him for the first time since he had entered her room. 'So you do know where I came from?'

'Yes, an orphanage in the city of Boston. You grew up there and were not adopted because the lady in charge was fond of you. She is now dead and you are quite alone in the world—but for me. For me, Arabel!'

For him . . . a man whose will would be as unbending as a bar of iron. She didn't want to be his, but the fingers holding hers were unrelentingly possessive.

'Please—tell me more about this lady who kept me with her at the orphanage.' Arabel tried to keep her voice as steady as possible, but combined with what he had said his touch was so nerve-racking, his physical nearness so disturbing. It was as if some powerful and barely restrained force was close to her, and it did nothing to make her feel protected or loved . . . loved with tenderness. If what he said about the orphanage was true, then she really did have cause to feel she was alone and at the mercy of a demanding stranger.

'I know very little about her,' he replied, and a frown had drawn his black brows into a slant above the hard thrust of his Latin nose. 'It would appear that she was good to you and made sure that you were well enough educated to earn a satisfactory living. When you were about sixteen she fell sick and had to go and live in a warmer climate, so she took you to California with her, where it was very possible you first learned to speak such excellent Spanish. After she died it seems you worked in Texas for a while, graduating from there to Venezuela to be the secretary of one of the directors.'

'So inevitably it all comes back to—to what happened in Venezuela,' she said. 'I can't recall a thing about my past—my mind is like a blank sheet of paper, the kind with secret writing that I—I keep hoping will suddenly become distinct to me. Oh, what shall I do if I don't remember anything?'

'You will not worry about it.' Don Cortez almost clipped the words. 'You will come and live at San Devilla with me and you will make a new life for yourself.'

'That's easy enough for you to say.' Arabel resented his decisive tone of voice and his seeming lack of sympathy. 'Can't you put yourself into my mind?'

'I have only to look into your eyes to be able to do that.' A tinge of irony came into his voice. 'I see fear there, and a distrust of my motives. You imagine I am feeding you with lies because you don't want to believe the truth, but inevitably you must accept the truth, that you belong to me and will be taken care of by me.'

'Have—have you been my lover?' Colour rushed into her face as she spoke and his gaze narrowed as he looked at her. 'Even that I can't remember—even something like that!'

'Something you might want to reject if you truly believe that you hated me,' he said, with a twist to his lips.

'Tell me!' Her eyes met his, wildly. 'I have to know!'

'Then you shall know.' His hand tightened on hers and his fingers were dark against her lighter skin, vibrant and sinewy as the rest of him, and calloused across the palm as if he did a great deal of riding on those horses he bred on his Andalusian estate. His touch was like a heated brand to Arabel, putting his mark upon her as he would put it upon his bulls.

He looked down into her eyes, holding her mesmerised, and yet mocking her for the tremor that she couldn't control. 'On the eve of our marriage we left Venezuela almost at once, pausing only long enough to collect some of your belongings from your apartment. We took a cab to the airfield and boarded a jet aircraft to the south of Spain . . . it was upon the flight that you suffered delayed shock and when we landed you were a sick girl and had to be brought to the hospital by ambulance. We are man and wife, *querida*, but we have not yet slept in each other's arms—if that is what you wanted me to state in black and white?'

'Yes.' She barely breathed the word. 'If our marriage is just something in writing, then we can seek an annulment and I can return to America. We're still almost single people—nothing has happened that might cause me to have your child, which I know would make it binding for you as a Latin. As things are we can be free of each other—can't we?'

Her blue eyes pleaded with his single eye. 'You can't deny me my release, for there's every chance that I shall regain my memory if I go home to America. You can't insist that I stay with you when I don't even know you!'

'Time, *querida*, will remedy that state of affairs.' His tone of voice was as adamant as his face, and the black patch somehow intensified his ruthless quality. Arabel shuddered and couldn't abide the vision of what lay behind that patch, and tearing her hand from his she covered her eyes in order to shut out his face.

'Y-you give me the horrors,' she gasped. 'I can hardly bear to look at you, l-let alone face the thought of—of living with you!'

'You are being childish.' The words seemed to leave the sting of a lash in their wake. 'But you aren't a child, Arabel. You are a young woman and you must face up to the future in a responsible manner. You owe it to me that you aren't still in a dirty prison cell and at the mercy of creatures who don't hesitate to torture women in order to wring information from them. Those men could easily have taken you for a member of the rebel cause to which those students were attached, and used upon your body implements of horrifying pain and degradation. You concealed those students, did you not? A pair of young fools who caused a great deal of chaos when they turned that oil refinery into a blazing inferno.'

Don Cortez paused and allowed his words to sink into her mind, and it seemed to Arabel that his face was cruel in that moment, as if he would also like to know why she had given refuge to those young men.

'Were they Americans like myself?' she asked.

'It seems that one of them had been educated in America before he returned to Venezuela to complete his studies at a Latin university. The other young hothead was a native of the country . . . you have no recollection of either of them?'

'None.' She shook her head, which had begun to ache. This Spaniard wasn't going to release her from their marriage, and right now she felt too tired and dispirited to fight his intentions. At the moment he was in control of the situation and all she could do was submit, and hope later on to find some means of escape from him.

'If you're prepared to put up with a wife who doesn't know you, or even like you, then that is your problem, Don Cortez. I realise that I have to go somewhere when they discharge me from the hospital, so it might as well be San Devilla—I suppose.'

As she spoke Arabel felt the sudden tension of the man . . . oh no, she thought wildly, don't let him kiss me . . . don't! But he merely rose to his feet and inclined his head in a distant way. '*Adios* for now,' he said, and there was something in his sudden dignity that made her think of a cavalier swinging his cloak about his shoulders. 'Rest yourself and try not to be anxious. There is time enough for you to remember if you hated me . . . or loved me.'

Never! The cry was silent and swift as a knife through her very nerves. She felt utterly certain that there had never been that kind of tenderness between them . . . love was a warm and passionate attachment of the body, a wonder of the senses, a certainty of the heart that loneliness was just a painful word.

All she felt was a cold apprehension, and a certainty buried deep in her like a barb that she had rejected this man who later on came to her in prison and used her predicament to bind her to him in this loveless relationship. There had never been a voluntary surrender from her; his will had been too strong for her there in that awful place and he had got his way because she had been too stricken to resist him.

'Hasta luego, querida.' With these words he was gone and Arabel was alone with the striped sunlight, the ticking of the clock, and the echo of his deep, vibrant voice calling her his darling in Spanish.

CHAPTER THREE

THERE was a breathtaking impact of brilliant foliage and flowers burning under a gold sun, and outlined against the luminous sky the rambling, broken walls of an old castle that might at the fall of night be haunted by the dark-avized lord and the clink of an anklet as the harem favourite ran eternally through the moonlight.

Peasant farmers wended their way across the fields, riding sturdy little donkeys or leading them along because their haunches were already laden with panniers. These *burros* were adorned with blue or gold tassels and there was an ageless quality to the sun-seamed faces of the farmers in their floppy straw hats.

The village houses were set in rows, their walls a thick crusted white in the sunlight, with jutting iron-laced balconies hung with geraniums and jasmine and assorted vines.

The large dove-coloured car sped smoothly on its way, passing all these essentially Spanish scenes at a smooth pace so that Arabel could take note of them and find them interesting. Don Cortez sat a little apart from her on the wide and comfortable rear seat, while a glass partition separated them from the uniformed chauffeur, a lean and exceedingly good-looking young Spaniard who had stared at Arabel when she had entered the car upon leaving the hospital.

Her husband didn't drive, she supposed, because of being blind on his left side. It still gave her an icy feeling at the pit of her stomach whenever she saw that black patch, and she was relieved that he sat so that his right profile was towards her. The aversion she felt for his infirmity was very disturbing. Was she, then, a finicky person? One of those who didn't like scars and handicaps in other people? Her fingers clenched together, for she didn't want to be that type of person, but each time Don Cortez looked directly at her she had to force herself to look away from him. She had a dread of what lay behind that dark patch, and she hoped fervently that he didn't remove it when he retired to bed.

She gazed from the car window at the village houses with layers of whitewash crusting their walls. Hardly anyone was about in the narrow byways that passed for streets, and she supposed that it was siesta time, a custom which had been followed at the hospital when the netting was drawn around the beds and everything fell very quiet while the hot sun held sway over the afternoon hours.

That they were driving through the heat was an indication to Arabel of her husband's eagerness to get her home to San Devilla, and luckily his expensive car was air-conditioned and she was clad in the lightly flowered chiffon which had been delivered to her only that morning. She felt cool enough and several miles back the Don had removed his jacket and sat beside her in the informality of white shirt and dark trousers.

'Smoke if you wish, *señor*.' She said it suddenly, with a slight touch of impatience, sensing that he was being controlled on this point because she had just left hospital. 'I really shan't curl up like a paper flower from a whiff of cigar smoke.'

'How do you know that I smoke cigars?'

'I—well, don't you? You seem so very Spanish, and one associates cigars with men of affluence. Look at your car, your chauffeur, and this expensively simple dress you bought for me.'

'You are mine to dress, aren't you?' He drew a slim leather case from a back pocket of his trousers and flipped it open. It contained several long dark-leaved cigars, one of which he thrust between his lips. The wheel of his lighter spun and the flame leapt to meet the cigar, and as he drew on it the aroma filled the car and Arabel tensed as the smoke drifted her way. Was it familiar or was it only an illusion?

They drove past a church of sandstone looming above the simple, almost primitive houses of this lost-in-time village. 'The *zocalo*,' he said. 'We should have been married in one such, and I have half a mind to have our ceremony church-blessed.'

'Is that really necessary?' She heard the note of panic in her own voice and knew that it gave away her secret hope that he would still relent and not insist that she stay married to him. 'I'm an American and hardly likely to be of your faith, *señor*.'

'As I told you once before, Arabel, we were married in my faith. Make no mistake, you are bound to me and will live with me in every meaning of the word. I don't plan to be regarded as a fond and impotent fool who keeps a beautiful woman in his house as merely a pet. No doubt such an arrangement would content you, and it might suit me if you had lank hair, crooked teeth and a spotty skin.' His lips quirked as he ran his glance over her features. 'Some time ago an old *bruja* was hanging about the arena where I was due to fight, and because most matadors are superstitious I didn't turn her away when she asked to predict my future. She took hold of my hand and studied the palm of it and I gave her a few coins to keep her happy, but she said some curious things which at the time I dismissed with a smile. She said I would lose several things precious to me and would regain only one of them during my lifetime. At Talavera some time after I had that encounter I had my eye gored out and I retired from the bullring. I took a journey in order to recover—well, let us say my pleasure in the look of a woman.'

He paused and the curls of smoke seemed to melt against his lean face, strong and brooding as carved stone. 'You can't imagine, *mi vida*, what pleasure it gives me just to look at you.'

'You can't imagine what I feel when I look at you!' The words leapt from Arabel's lips, as if she threw sharp pebbles in his face. His expression didn't alter. He was like stone and her words seemed to make no impact. He merely shrugged his shoulders and allowed the dark ash of his cigar to fall to the carpet of his car.

'The bridal jitters are a natural reaction,' he drawled. 'No doubt felt by other innocent females.'

'How can you be so sure that I'm innocent, Don Cortez?' A flame of defiance leapt in her eyes, and suddenly her face was spirited and alive within the *fleur de lys* frame of her hair. 'Don't forget that I concealed a pair of young men in my apartment—what if one of them was my lover?'

'Then too bad for you, *guapa*.' He spoke with a meaning flourish of his cigar. 'You have read of Othello, eh? Your mind plays tricks and lets you remember this type of knowledge—ah, I see that the name of the jealous Moor rings a bell. Do you recall his wife Desdemona, whom he smothered because he believed her faithless? You, *mi vida*, have a very slim and silky neck and I have Moro blood in my veins—as do many of the people living in this region of Spain. I trust I make myself explicit?'

'More than explicit, *señor*.' She looked at him with curious eyes. 'You would do it, wouldn't you, and yet any affair which I had before becoming your wife couldn't be called an act of adultery, unless you make your own laws?'

'Perhaps I do, Arabel.'

'How arrogant of you, *señor*! You said I was reared in an orphanage in America not in a convent in Spain where, presumably, the control over the inmates is very strict. If you had a *novia* from a convent then it would be reasonable to suppose that she was immaculate, but short of calling in your family physician to give me a thorough going over, how can you be certain that you haven't married shop-soiled goods? If you haven't, then can I really expect to be throttled by your very strong hands?'

He glanced at one of his hands as she said this, lean, dark, and no doubt very adept with the *muleta* and the sword. For an instant she could almost see him in the arena, a lean and lonely figure as he faced the bull in the final act of the fight. The crowd would fall silent as he cast a spell of doomed fascination, for this would be the moment of truth, to kill or die, man against an elemental force, his brain pitched against sheer brawn, his courage challenged to the hilt by the fearless, mindless stamina of a powerful animal. A nerve quickened in Arabel's throat . . . she knew in that instant that under his speckless shirt and his well-cut trousers Don Cortez's body carried scars, that his soul had been in jeopardy to wine and women. He had had a name which men had defended in the taverns with their knives . . . she felt the gliding of his *aguila* eye over her face, and then he had closed his hand over hers and she felt her skin burning from his touch.

'Having been no saint why should I expect you to have been an angel, eh?' His lips twisted cynically. 'For most of my life I knew only the kind of women who make gods and heroes of bullfighters. Is it so amazing that I should want my wife to be virtuous?'

'How can either of us be sure that I have virtue to give you?' she asked. 'I can't remember what kind of a person I was, and you threaten me if I prove to be —disappointing.'

He shrugged his shoulders. 'Let us not leap puddles in dry weather,' he drawled. 'I think I know women well enough to judge your moral character.'

'Many women, *señor*?' She wasn't really curious, only a little cynical.

'Enough.' Again he shrugged and took a hard pull on his cigar. 'Were you expecting a monk for a husband?'

'I wasn't expecting a husband at all, and I'd hardly expect a matador to have lived like a monk, not with death staring you in the face every few days.' She gave a sudden shiver. 'What a shocking way to earn a living! Was there nothing else for you to do?'

'I wanted to be well off,' he said curtly. 'In Spain the quickest way is by becoming an *espada* of reputation. That was what I became, but it ended at Talavera as I told you. That part of my life is over, so you don't have to shiver in your shoes and expect me home with blood on my cape. It is finished! I now run my own *estancia*, and there you will be the *duena*. A leap forward for a secretary, you must admit?'

'A great honour,' she said, and then winced as his fingers closed so hard on hers that her hand felt as if it had been put in a vice and was about to be crushed. 'God—you're cruel!' she gasped.

'I am probably everything you never wanted in the man you would live your life with,' he rejoined, slowly relaxing his fingers on her aching bones. 'But fate plays a role in all our lives and whether you wanted me or not, *mi vida*, you have me.'

Arabel bit her lip as his dark, gold-ringed eye seemed to bore into her. She felt as if an eagle had plucked her from out of nowhere and was carrying her off into a wild region of his own, there to make her share with him the nest which his killing gold had bought him. So he had been a very poor boy who had yearned to be rich, and she had to admit that his costly silk shirt sat well upon his hard shoulders, its whiteness throwing into contrast the natural swarthiness of his skin. Her eyes fixed themselves upon his throat and she saw the gleam of the fine chain that probably carried an engraved medal. He would be superstitious and yet at the same time he would rely entirely on his own ruthless resources to carry him through a *corrida*. It was the one single blessing that he no longer carried on his career as a matador. Arabel felt in her very bones that she couldn't have borne it had he still practised his deadly art. That at least she didn't have to endure.

'You are giving me the look of a tortured angel,' he gibed. 'Are you feeling hungry? I am in no doubt that you ate the breakfast of a bird.'

'Hungry?' She moistened her lips with the tip of her tongue. 'To tell you the truth, *señor*, I feel incredibly thirsty.'

'That we will soon remedy.' He leaned forward and slid open the glass partition that separated them from the driver. 'Mateo, please to stop the car for a few moments while you fetch the lunch basket from the boot. The *señora* and I will now take some refreshment.'

'*Si, señor.*' The car slid smoothly to a halt and Arabel watched as the young man in tailored beige went round to the back and took from the boot a solid-looking basket. He handed it into the car and once again she was conscious of his eyes upon her. So the members of the Don's staff were summing her up already, taking note of the fact that she wasn't Spanish, comparing her to the vivacious women their master would have known in the past . . . might still know, for there was every chance that a man of his age and reputation had kept a mistress.

'*Gracias.*' Don Cortez undid the straps of the basket and took from it a bottle of beer and a packet of sandwiches, which he handed to his driver. 'Have your own lunch, Mateo, but first find a more shady situation for the car.'

A few minutes later they were parked in the shade of a wall over which leaned the trunks of several palm trees. Over the broken stones rambled a strange looking ground-vine to which was attached some gourds of a bright orange colour.

'The apples of Sodom,' said the Don as he handed her a tulip-shaped glass of pale gold wine. 'When the wind blows they float along like coloured balloons.'

'Thank you, *señor.*' She took a grateful sip of the wine and found it light and just faintly sweet. 'They are odd-looking, and these palm trees make me think of the desert.'

'You are now in a region, *querida*, to which the invading men of the desert brought their Islamic culture and their palms. Andalusians are still haunted by all that was Moorish; it is in their music, their houses, and their patios. It is in their way of thinking, especially with regard to women.'

He handed her a napkin wrapped around a wing of turkey, and there was a deep crevice in his brown cheek.

'Are you telling me that you run your household on the harem principle?' she asked smartly. 'Am I expected to live in seclusion, and to go about your house with a veil across my face?'

'It would make a pretty picture, eh?' He took a deep bite of his turkey leg, gave a slight frown and amply sprinkled the meat with dark pepper. 'Would you like some of this, Arabel?'

'No, thanks.' She nibbled at her own meat and watched him attack his food with frank appetite. He drank beer himself, straight from the bottle, and somehow it didn't offend her that he made no pretence of being the polite and dainty host. He was utterly and completely a man, she thought, and she felt the blood come tingling into her cheeks as she speculated on what that would mean with regard to her. If she had hoped for compromise, for patience, for the restraint of a cool man, then she hoped in vain.

'More wine?' He held the bottle above her glass and after a moment's hesitation she complied and let him refill her glass. It might help to take the raw edge off her apprehension, for she suspected that they weren't all that far from San Devilla and once she entered the confines of his *estancia* she might as well regard herself as much in his power as those women whom the Moors had kept for their pleasure. Those old strains were most definitely in the man who sat beside her, biting now into a pie of meat and onion, which he had sliced into two portions, one for her.

'Come, eat,' he said. 'It is good food and you need to be built up after your ordeal.'

'My ordeal has only just begun,' she said defiantly.

'With wine and roast bird in the shade of a palm tree?' he mocked. 'You pay your husband some delightful compliments, don't you, *querida*? Am I such an ogre and a roughneck merely because I wear a patch over a destroyed eye?'

Her fingers clenched the stem of her wine-glass. 'You will keep assuming that everything is normal, but for me all this is like a strange dream from which I can't wake up. If only I could trust you——'

'You still have doubts about me?' He pressed a napkin to his lips and stared at her.

'Yes,' she admitted. 'I feel as if you're holding back something which might suddenly shift the cloud from my mind. I—I believe you want it this way! It suits you to have me in a state of forgetfulness!'

'Oh, and why is that?' His voice was as smooth as velvet, but his black brows had drawn together in a pair of slanting lines.

'Because when I start to remember I shall know for certain why it is that I hate being your wife.'

'*Gracias, mi vida*, another gem of flattery from a fond and grateful girl.' His lips curled. 'Why do I bother with such as you when I can get for myself a charming and affectionate Andalusian who would be only too happy to share my home with me?'

'I share your sentiments, Don Cortez. Why bother with me when I'm obviously a cold little fish?'

'*Ay*, a goldfish who swam into shark waters and had to be hooked out before they maltreated you. For that at least be grateful. You wouldn't have liked the feel of an electric rod along your spine!'

'Don't!' She shuddered. 'It was good of you to drag me out of that, but did you have to go to the extreme of marrying me? Wouldn't they have released me any other way? Couldn't you have gone to the American Consulate and told them I had been arrested?'

'It would all have taken too much time. I had a certain prestige in Venezuela and so I used it, flourishing a priest in their faces and being altogether the passionate and distracted lover.'

Her heart jolted at that word. 'What of the two students, *señor*? Could you do nothing to help them?'

'They weren't my concern, and had I interfered on their behalf I should have lost my chance of whisking you out from under the noses of the prison guards.' He gave a sudden click of his fingers, almost a gesture of contempt. 'Those hot-headed fools had caused a serious fire and endangered the lives of people living in the vicinity of the oil refinery, and it hardly helps political unrest by creating that kind of holocaust. The wise man uses his head, not his spleen.'

'So—here we are.' Arabel sipped her wine, for she hadn't much appetite for the food. 'Two people facing life together and barely in sympathy with each other. I'm darned sure that I'd never marry a bullfighter from choice!'

'I told you, Arabel, I am no longer an *espada.* I own land and breed livestock, and that is how you will think of me, as the *dueno* of San Devilla. You will dismiss from your mind that I had any other profession. You will forget it.'

'As I've forgotten everything else?' she sighed. 'Like an infant, almost, I must start from scratch—but you won't treat me like an infant, will you? You'll insist that I be a wife to you in every sense of the word!'

'You're an adult female.' He spoke curtly and ripped an orange in two, the juice running out over his sun-darkened skin. He raised his hand and licked off the juice . . . like a great cat grooming its pelt, she thought. A puma of lithe and unpredictable impulses, with every sinew moving like silk under that tawny skin. 'You know as well as I that we can't live in close conjunction in the same house and not be aware of each other. I should have to quarter you at the other side of San Devilla, and I don't intend to do so. Why should I arouse speculation as to my abilities to be a husband to a young woman of undoubted desirability? You don't know Andalusians and how innate is their curiosity about newlyweds, and I have a fairly large staff of servants, not to mention several relatives who reside at the *estancia*. I don't intend to be classed with a castrated bull, not for you or any other woman!'

'I'm certain,' she gave a sudden nervous laugh, 'that no one would ever take you for anything of the kind.'

'Exactly so, and I don't intend to add any fuel to even a thread of smoke.' He tossed a quarter of orange into his mouth and there was a sort of arrogance that was very Latin in the way he lifted his well-marked chin. 'A Spanish household is a more open affair than it might be in America. You will be expected to be seen in my bedroom, as I shall be expected to wander freely in and out of yours. Our rooms are adjoining, and also our bathroom will be shared . . . do you honestly suppose, Arabel, that I could see you in a state of attractive undress and not react in the way that nature intended? Stone you called me, but I am not made of it . . . and you are no statue yourself.'

'W-what do you mean by that?' She stared at him, feeling the flurry of nerves deep inside her.

'You are white flesh and warm blood, and let me prove it.' As he spoke he reached out and drew his fingers down the soft inner side of her left arm. She gave a little gasp, for his touch was knowing, like the fingers of a guitarist playing over a finely tuned instruments that he meant to play to its finest pitch.

'Don't!' She drew her arm away and he didn't try to prevent her. He merely smiled, a man who knew women as she knew only a blankness when it came to men. If her innocent, even coy reaction to his touch was any true indication then she had never known any of the ultimates in lovemaking. She was—chaste. An old-fashioned term, but she sensed that it applied in her case, and there was a look on the Don's face that echoed her realisation. She was his! His to take and teach, and he had faced *el toro* too often to be concerned about an unwilling wife.

'Do you always get your own way?' she cried at him.

'Whenever possible,' he drawled. 'You'll fight me, of course, but that's only to be expected.'

'Y-you won't spare me at all?' Her eyes blazed blue into his. 'Not even if I plead with you to—to give me time to get accustomed to you and your way of life? It would be the courteous thing, and after all, you like to be addressed as Don!'

'True, because there are many things that can be bought with money, but I wasn't born a gentleman, *guapa*, so don't try appealing to instincts I may not have. I was dragged up in the back alleys of Seville and my education was learned at the back doors of the *torero* quarters and in the smoky dens where the flamenco gipsies danced the night away. My mother was a slut and I never knew my father, though she always swore he was a visiting Castilian who took a fancy to her face. I suppose she was pretty when a girl, but I only remember her as an untidy, black-haired slattern who hung about the men who frequented the bars where she danced. She died when I was twelve, of a knife-thrust in a dark patio, and I then became a runabout at the arenas and then a very youthful *torero* who went through every phase of the *corrida* life. I knew dirt, hunger, pain and pleasure at an age when the sons of Dons are still being pampered by their sisters and taught by tutors. I received my first *cornada* at the age of fifteen and was nursed back to health by the *prima mia* of a local brothel.

'There,' he leaned forward into Arabel's eyes, 'is my early history for you to mull over, so don't talk again about appealing to my gentler instincts. I have very few!'

Arabel gazed at him, not really shocked by what he had revealed about himself, for it was there in his hard-bitten face that he had known a life that had not always been smooth. He had lived and learned and grown rich out of danger, and she didn't condemn him for any of that, only for his insistence that she live with him as if she loved him.

'Must you treat all women so ruthlessly, *señor*, because your mother gave you so little affection?'

'You think she didn't care for me?' A smile touched his lips. 'She did in her careless fashion, and I do assure you that I haven't gone through life being a brute to women. On the contrary, I have known one or two who shed quite a bit of sunshine for me whenever I emerged from the clamour of the *corrida*.'

'Yet you stayed unmarried,' Arabel murmured. 'Why was that?'

'When there are many sweets to choose from a man sometimes gets a taste for something with a bite to it.'

'Me?' She gazed at him with uncertain eyes.

'You would sooner bite me than kiss me, eh?'

'Ours doesn't promise to be a very tender relationship, does it, *señor*?'

He moved his hands expressively. 'Tenderness is for old age, when to be solicitous and considerate is nearly all that a man and a woman can be to each other. If you have eaten all that you require, Arabel, then we'll resume our journey.' He tapped the glass panel and indicated to his chauffeur that lunch was concluded. As the car started up with hardly any vibration from its engine the Don re-strapped the basket and set it on one side. He sat back and his lean fingers played with his cigar case.

'Are we very nearly—there?' she asked, and it was impossible to keep the nervous note out of her voice.

He glanced from the window and slid a cigar from his case. 'In about half an hour we will be home,' he said, and his teeth gripped the dark slim Havana. 'That is how you will think of San Devilla, and not as a kind of prison house where I plan to apply torture. I merely plan to live as other men live, with a woman I find attractive who will one day supply me with a child or two.'

Arabel caught her breath audibly. He said it so matter-of-factly, as if he didn't intend her amnesia to be any kind of barrier to his own requirements. To the devil with her mind, that was his attitude. She had a face and a shape that appealed to him and that was all that mattered.

'You're as hard as nails,' she gasped.

'Of course,' he drawled, through a mouthful of smoke. 'I am everything your imagination likes to make of me, and above all I'm your husband.'

'A—a husband who cared tuppence about a sick wife would consider her feelings!'

'You aren't sick in body, Arabel, nor in mind. You have forgotten a slice of your past history, that is all, and I don't intend to pamper in you the idea that you're too fragile to be touched. I know differently.'

'You know—what?' She gave him a strained look. 'You drop hints but never tell me outright what you know about me. Were we acquainted before this happened to me? Had I met you?'

'We met.' He shrugged his shoulders and looked infuriatingly casual.

'Were we—friends?' Her heart was banging in her side like a drum.

'No.' He studied the dark ash on the end of his cigar, then flicked it from the open window. 'You could never have called us friends.'

'Then I didn't like you when I—I knew you before?'

'I would hardly say you liked me.' His face was an inscrutable mask as he glanced at her, and the dark patch made him menacing. 'Anyway, to be liked is a tepid state of affairs—there is no passion in it.'

'But there is passion in being hated?' she breathed, and felt the conviction building in her that she had hated him, the lean *espada* whose hands had been dipped in blood.

'Almost as much as in being love,' he drawled. 'As you have guessed, I am no halfway man and you may hate me or love me, Arabel, but don't bother me with any in-between emotions. Let us say that my kind of life has excluded them—the black shadows and the blazing sunlight have put their mark on me. I have walked in one or the other too long to be able to change old habits.'

'And doesn't it worry you, Don Cortez, one little bit, to be driving to your home with a wife who doesn't love you?'

'Do I look worried?' he mocked, and he ran his eye over her slender figure in the cool flowered chiffon. 'Here in the south we say of a delectable girl that she is the taste of cinnamon, the tang of the lemon, the fig among green leaves. You belong to me and that is all I care about, and right now is the moment when I shall return to you something that you returned to me.'

He leaned forward to where his jacket lay and took something from one of the inner pockets. There was a click as he opened a jewel case, a shimmer of gems, a waterfall of blue across the skirt of her dress as he reached for her right wrist and gripped it so she couldn't pull away. In a kind of fascination she watched him, his smoking cigar clenched in his teeth, lean fingers locking about her wrist a bracelet of chain-linked sapphires that glowed against her skin like chinks of dazzling blue sky.

He held up her wrist and smiled quizzically. 'A pretty thing, the eyes of Arabel strung upon a chain of gold.'

'Don't!' She quivered at the description, at the gift, at his remark about having had this bracelet returned to him by her. So when he first met her, no doubt through the man for whom she had worked, he had presented her with this costly piece of jewellery and she had refused to accept it. Now he would insist because she was no longer the secretary of another man, an independent girl working for her living who had the right to refuse whatever he offered. She could feel his grip against her wristbone and knew he had the strength and the temper to break her bones if he so wished.

'I don't ask you to thank me for it, *guapa*, but this time you will wear it and like it. Do you hear me?'

'Yes! And why was it given in the first place? Because you hoped to buy me as you've bought so many women?' Her eyes were as burning blue as the gems, and she suddenly heard him catch his breath and saw the leaping into life of a pulse beside his mouth.

'You were never to be bought and I never tried.' He spoke gratingly, in his throat. 'Let it suffice that I saw a pair of blue eyes and thought to make an offering to them; let me add that pretty as the gems are, they are no match for what nature put into your face.' With these words he carried her hand to his lips and she felt them slide warm and firm across her skin, across her knuckles and then into the palm, where they stayed buried for a breathless moment.

In that moment her head seemed to swim and her knees went curiously slack . . . he made of kissing her palm an intimacy beyond description . . . as if his lips were silently telling her that so would he kiss her on other parts of her body.

She strove not to snatch her hand away from him; she endured what he did, what he implied, what he warned was in store for her as his wife. He was a Spaniard and she belonged to him, and the bracelet was the symbolic chain of his ownership.

The car sped on through the heat of the afternoon and every turn of the road brought them closer to his *estancia*. The dream of his youth, when all he had possessed was his nerve and the driving ambition never to be poor or hungry ever again. Then, having acquired his land and his house, he had looked around for a wife to share them with. His appetite sated by the kind of women who had flung themselves into his arms, he had decided to try his technique on a less willing girl . . . just for the devilish enjoyment of it . . . a retired matador who still needed excitement in his life, and challenge.

She was to be his challenge and there was every indication that he was already enjoying this new sort of *corrida* . . . this more subtle game of stalking a female until the moment of truth came for both of them.

CHAPTER FOUR

ARABEL sat there beside Don Cortez in tense silence, drifting tendrils of his cigar smoke evoking vague memories that she had now become afraid of. Somewhere beyond the haze of her amnesia lay the reason why she was here beside him . . . panic, a twist of terror, a scream held in her throat as just ahead of the car there appeared some towering columns and a pair of massive iron gates.

The gates opened silently and automatically as the car approached, and Arabel turned her head to gaze back at the gates, as if her freedom were lost beyond them, and she saw that the overhead section of them was wrought into some kind of a device . . . the head of a bull resting upon the blade of a sword, with an iron fist gripping the hilt.

'How appropriate!' The words leapt to her lips and emerged half-strangled.

'Indeed,' he drawled, and without looking at him Arabel sensed that his lips were drawn into a sardonic smile. 'The escutcheon of the house of Ildefonso de la Dura.'

'Is the grand name also an invention of your own?' she inquired.

'Part of it,' he admitted, with a shrug. 'My mother was of the Ildefonso gipsy tribe, so I'm entitled to that, at least.'

His car sped along a wide driveway with fields at

either side, and Arabel saw the bulls of San Devilla standing in groups, looking like the great animals of Mithras, powerful and significant, and yet quite serene in the sunlight. Did they sense, she wondered, that from this ranch they wouldn't be sent to the arenas to die by the sword?

It was strange that Don Cortez should safeguard his own bulls from that cruel destiny, for she wouldn't have thought that he had very much compassion or sensitivity in his hard bones. Unless he had learned over the years to respect and admire the courage of possibly the most noble animal in the history of man.

Arabel's hands were gripped together, almost in an attitude of prayer, the sun agleam in the sapphires of his ring and bracelet. His fingers closed upon her arm and she quivered in every nerve. 'Now we approach the house whose every stone and beam is mine!'

A great moon-shaped archway cast its shadow, faced with lovely old tiles that seemed to have collected sun and sky and moonlight into their surfaces, and they drove into a huge patio where a great number of flowerpots hung in wire frames, from which spilled numerous flowers on green tendrils against thick white walls. The kind of walls erected by the Moors to keep out intruders . . . and to keep their women secluded.

The car drove around a central fountain of tawny stone, with at its base a great basin filled with lily-buds and the flicker of golden fish tails.

Shading the fountain was an enormous tree, a towering giant whose branches were laden with wreaths of bell-flowers, living cups of sheer gold beauty, spilling down almost to the ground.

Arabel caught her breath in wonder, and then she felt the Don's breath stir against her left ear. 'This is our garden of the golden bells,' he murmured. 'On moonlit nights you might hear the faintest of music and you might wonder a little about the magic of life.'

'If one heard music here,' she rejoined, 'then it would be the clink of golden links on the captive feet of a Moor's slave girl. This is a Moorish house, is it not, *señor*?'

'In every detail,' he agreed. 'Down to the veiltail fish who swim in their own veils, twirling and twisting like the ghosts of those slave girls.'

He laughed as the car came to a halt, flanked by half-moon arcades leading into the house itself. The chauffeur opened the door beside the Don, who alighted with that economy of movement the matador had to possess if he wished to survive. He held out a lean hand to Arabel and after a moment's hesitation she accepted it and allowed him to assist her from the cushioned interior of the car to the sunlit flagstones of the lovely old patio.

She stood there bemused, still unable to link all this to reality. She was lost in a dream and would surely awake to quite different surroundings. It couldn't really be true that she was the *duena* of this place ... dazedly she looked around her, breathing the scents of the many flowers and seeing above the main area of the *estancia* a kind of tower of white stone inset with many small windows, rising to a pagoda-like roof.

'That is what we call a *mirador*,' said Don Cortez, following the direction of her gaze. 'A picturesque cage for a woman, eh?'

'Is that where you plan to put me?' she asked, and she wasn't joking.

'No, I plan to put you within reach of my hand,' he said mockingly. 'We don't often use the *mirador*, because the stairway has grown unsafe, and the place merely adds a touch of charm to the main building. Shall we go in? Members of the household will be taking siesta so you will be able to acquaint yourself with the house before you need meet the family, who take *merienda* at four, which is a sort of teatime.'

'I see.' Arabel had tautened as he mentioned his family. 'Have you many relatives living here with you, *señor*?'

'My aunt and her children, and a cousin who works for me. Also a friend or two from the old days who like to be among the bulls and the horses and have little else to do with their time. You will soon get to know everybody—and now let me show you the interior of your home.'

Your home! The words went through her, for though she couldn't deny that this old thick-walled *estancia* had a quaint air of gravity and grace about it, nonetheless it was a strange place to her and she was going to find it difficult to think of it as her home, where she was going to have to live in intimacy with the man who walked at her side. It had a breathless effect on her, walking beside him into the shade of the cool arcades where the air was fragrant from a great shrub whose scarlet petals were like splashes of blood against the white walls, and where even here the metallic churring of countless cicadas could be heard, unseen and yet constantly in tune with each other.

They entered a sort of hall that ran the length of the house, with the filigreed shadows of lamps hung on chains, immense blackwood cabinets that might have been chiselled from the trees in one great piece, so firm and enduring did they look, and tall chairs upholstered in Spanish leather the colour of wine. Ornately framed mirrors reflected the hall and its furniture, and there were sculptures of bronze and steel on the cabinet tops.

Arabel looked about her with the wide, almost frightened eyes of a lost child. A sort of terror took hold of her, for there was something about this house that hinted at wild loves, haunting voices, tears of grief as well as cries of joy. It was old, old, and the shades of the past clung to it, and its walls held captive the ways and attitudes of those bygone days. Her own land, America, might have been a million miles away. The freedom of the modern woman would be a myth in this land of white sunlight and black shadows . . . of men in whose veins ran the passions and cultures of their Islamic past.

Don Cortez led her to a spiral of openwork stairs that led upwards to a gallery whose curving walls were a mosaic, like something out of a Moorish palace. He opened a pair of massive cedarwood doors that were embellished by intricate carving, and as Arabel stepped into the apartment she was smitten again by the combination of beauty and the oriental desire to shut out the world with meshes of iron and great silvery slabs of wood.

Those doors closed behind her like the gates of a prison, and she spun round to stare at the Don, standing there with his shoulders to the slabs of carved cedarwood, a lean, matador figure, made extra menacing by that patch of black velvet over what he had called his destroyed eye. The other eye, fierce and vital in his dark face, was fixed upon her in a kind of triumph, as if for a long time he had dreamed of seeing a fair and alien woman in his bedroom.

'Oh, I quite agree,' he drawled, 'there are many disasters which can overcome a woman and an unwanted marriage is probably high on the list. But all the same you have to put up with it, and if you are a bird in a gilded cage, *querida*, you must admit that it's a large one.'

He gestured towards lovely iron doors leading into the further realms of the apartment. 'This is the master bedroom, and beyond lies a sitting-room for you, a dressing-room and a bathroom. We are completely self-contained . . . completely private.'

Arabel felt suddenly chilled in her light dress, and then suddenly there was a relaxed, almost sensual expression about his lips, and aware of what he was thinking her skin began to burn, and she glanced about her like a hunted thing, seeking some means of escape from the tough strong arms that were entitled to take possession of her any time he felt the urge.

Her gaze—and it would have to happen—fell on the bed whose great headboard was carved with satyrs. She quickly looked elsewhere at beautiful marquetry corner-cupboards and lamps on black onyx bases. Her nostrils tensed to a fragrance of beeswax, for each item of furniture seemed to glow.

'Well?' he murmured. 'Have you nothing to say?'

'It must be like sleeping in a museum,' she shot back at him, for she didn't dare to be affected by the sensuous beauty of the lace bed-throw, the deep-piled oriental carpet, the sheer gauze—like a bridal veil—fixed by rings to the bedposts in readiness for the semi-tropical night-time, when the tall ribbed shutters would be flung wide to let in the air and the countless flying insects of a southern region.

'Museums are dead places, *mi vida*.' He strolled to one of the corner cupboards and stood looking at a blue and gold Madonna who sat in one of the niches. 'I assure you that I am very much alive and that I fully intend to share this room with you. Personally speaking, I quite like it, especially when I think back to a boyhood when I sometimes spent the night on a pile of straw in someone's stable. It gives me a kick, shall I say, to feel soft linen sheets against my skin.'

Arabel's pulses set up a soft pounding in her veins. He told her without actually putting it into words that he slept in his own tawny skin, that lean body sheer with well-trained muscle, with horn scars, and the hard masculine drives of his dominant nature. Nothing had ever really conquered him, and here in this vast Spanish bedroom in her flimsy chiffon dress Arabel felt more defenceless than ever when confronted by this *espada* in his very own environs.

'Is there really any virtue in resistance?' Don Cortez asked, his voice wickedly soft and seductive. 'Does the woman struggle against the man . . . or herself?'

'I'm struggling to know myself,' she rejoined. 'Do you fondly imagine that I have a secret self who wishes to be overcome by you? The very way you earned all this chills my blood. Bullfighting is barbaric, which proves that you are basically uncivilised.'

'You don't say?' He looked amused, standing there with his hands halfway in the pockets of his tailored trousers, his silk shirt open at his throat, outwardly suave and inwardly savage . . . Arabel was certain of that. 'The *corrida* is to the Spaniard what the fist fight is to the American.' His white teeth seemed to bite on the words.

'In such a fight it's man against man,' she retaliated.

'And that in your estimation is civilised?' he mocked. 'It seems far more primitive to me, *guapa*, to bloody the nose of a human opponent and possibly destroy his pride with a leather glove. A real fighting bull is a creature of immense strength and stature, fearless and at times marvellously challenging.'

'You mean he's a powerful sexual symbol which

man has to slaughter because he can't match it.' Arabel flung up her chin and felt the heat in her face.

'So you admit the sexual symbolism, eh? Do you admit any of the beauty of the capework and the agility of man and beast?'

'Pagan male launched against a bull—that is considered beautiful?' She spoke and looked scornful, and thrust down inside her the sudden realisation that before the gouging out of his left eye Don Cortez would have had a gaze almost oriental in its charisma. The right eye intent upon her was as if carved out of onyx with a touch of sheerest gold . . . a sign if she needed one that the Moor ran strong in his veins, giving him that touch of ruthless fatalism that would always have followed him into the hot, sanded arena.

'As a pair, *mi vida*, matador and bull have a certain pride, unlike wrestlers and boxers who grunt and sweat their way through a tournament and emerge battered and bitter.'

'The bull hardly emerges as an object of beauty, more one of pity with barbs in him . . . ugh, it's brutal! You're a brute for having been part of it . . . was it fun, master matador, when the horn struck your face and half blinded you?'

He stood there in utter stillness just looking at her, searching her face with his single eye. 'You speak so emotionally, Arabel, that you might have been there.'

'I can imagine it.' She gave a shudder and looked away from him. 'Have you no feelings? Has every bit of human pity been gouged out of you as well?'

'You want me to pity you?' He began to come towards her, slowly and almost with feline grace, as if for him this bedroom had become an arena and she an object for him to torment cruelly for his own amusement, instead of that of the crowd.

Arabel backed away from his approach, gasping

as she felt the edge of the bed against the back of her legs. Suddenly everything was dangerous and there was no escape from this man who hadn't feared bulls, let alone a woman. She threw up a hand as if to defend herself and the chain of sapphires blazed against her skin and matched her eyes.

'W-what are you going to do?' It was probably the most foolish question she could have flung at him, for he threw back his head and gave a grating laugh. He reached for her, drew her hard against him and held her so she felt every line and muscle of him. He put up a hand and stroked it over her hair. 'My El Dorado, mine. How can you know how I have dreamed of such a moment, to hold my woman in my arms in my very own house? Clean, sweet, like fresh-plucked corn, with no awareness of the filth and agony that can lurk in the dark corners of this life. How on earth could I leave you to become dirty and demoralised in a foreign prison? Anything was worth the price I might have to pay . . . even your hatred of me, *querida*. Even that. Anything is surely worth the price that I ask you to pay?'

His arm was like a band of iron about her, pressing just close enough to let her know that he could bruise her and break her, if he so wished. Letting her feel the strength and the ardour that was rampant in every sinew of his lean body.

'The physical price?' she asked scornfully. 'Aren't you man enough to save a woman without demanding that she give in to your—desires?'

'If I were less of a man, Arabel, I might be content to take less from you and to treat you like a sister.' He lowered his face to hers and put his warm lips against the silky side of her neck . . . his lips were burning, like those of a man who had gone parched in a desert. The awareness shocked through her that she aroused in him a need that was close to what a thirsting man might feel. His lips searched her skin as if he wanted to get to the very essence of her, and every nerve inside her was clamouring its alarm as she felt his mouth inside the soft chiffon that covered her collarbones. He seemed to be nibbling on her as if he liked the very taste of her and it was—it was primitive, and she had to get away from it before he drove her mad.

She beat at him, twisted and turned in his arms, and all he did was laugh at her struggles and ignore them. His breath was warm against her skin that he had bared with his marauding lips, and he said into her very ear:

'I'm going to teach you to want my kisses, *querida*, and then I'm going to make you want me.'

'Brute ... killer ... arrogant swine!' She beat at him and it was like bashing her hands against a stone wall. He merely laughed in his throat and threw her on to the bed. He leaned over her and his single eye seemed like a flame in his face ... desperately she clawed up at him and her fingers felt something and dragged at it.

The velvet patch came away from his face and Arabel screamed and the room went as empty as that eye socket and there were little red flashes in her brain, like those seams of puckered skin around that tiny awful crater in his face.

'No ... no ...!'

'Stop it!' He shook her. 'Hush, don't cry out like that! *Pequeña, pequeña*, you will hurt yourself!'

'Go away! I can't bear to look at you! It's awful ... awful!'

He leaned above her only a second more, and then he stood up and reached for the black patch which she had torn from his eye. He gripped it and turned away from her and in a whirling daze Arabel was aware that he was adjusting it over the empty socket in the bed of scars. She moaned and turned over on her face and lay there shivering. She had almost fainted and now a deathly kind of nausea had hold of her.

'Leave me alone,' she pleaded.

'As you wish.' There was a moment of silence, and then the sound of closing doors.

It was only then, after he had gone, that Arabel came to realise that she had been silly, spiteful and rather cruel. She sat up, pushing the disarranged hair from her eyes; there were tears on her face, but she had not been aware of any weeping. Oh God, everything was all so wrong—this marriage, being here with a man she was hopelessly unable to love. But all the same—she bit her lip and wiped away the wetness from her cheeks—it must have hurt enough when he had lost the eye without being told to his face that she found him unbearable to look at.

Arabel slid off the bed and went to the dressing-table, where she stared at her own distressed face in the great shield of a mirror. Was that the kind of person she was? Petulant and spiteful, and so coldly puritanical that she couldn't endure to be touched by *any* man?

She picked up a tortoiseshell comb that lay on the lace mat and drew it through her hair. She noticed the shining gold colour of her own hair and saw reflected her slim and gracefully curving shape in the chiffon dress. The neckline was still disarranged and she found herself touching the smooth skin of her neck, where he had touched it and pressed his lips.

She stared into her own eyes until she felt self-hypnotised. No, she wouldn't believe that she was cold and selfishly pitiless of anyone's deformities.

There was some other reason why she couldn't bear to be touched by Don Cortez, and all at once as she stood there, in the quiet luxury of this large bedroom, she seemed to be certain of that reason ... she had been in love! She had loved someone ... a dearly lost someone who lurked behind that infuriating curtain over her mind. Her conscience knew that there was another man in her life and that was why she reacted the way she did towards Don Cortez.

But oh, if there was another man whom she had loved, why hadn't he come forward to help her? Why had it to be this Spaniard who meant nothing to her?

She closed her eyes and strained to see that other face, but the blank dark curtain stayed in place even though she had become utterly certain that she had been in love with someone. The only explanation was that it had been one of the students. Arrested himself, he had been unable to help her, and now he was miles away and lost to her ... lost because she couldn't recall his name, or anything about him, and was now the lawful wife of a complete stranger.

Not quite a stranger, perhaps, for at some time Don Cortez had met her and presented her with the sapphire bracelet. She lifted her arm and fingered the blue gems, which she had returned to him because even then she had not wanted his attentions.

Now everything was reversed in his favour. She owed him her escape from prison ... owed him what he had every right and every intention of claiming ...

Herself!

His jewellery on her hand and wrist, a dress he had bought covering her body, the wide roof of San Devilla over her head, keeping out the sun, the rain, and all intruders. Arabel turned from the mirror and gazed around the room she must share with him, knowing him to be too inflexible to be put off from his purpose by her reaction to his blind eye. He was too tough-fibred to be deeply concerned about her feelings; his way of life would have hardened him beyond that kind of sensitivity. She was married to him and he meant that marriage to be a proper one, not some monastic affair with polite meetings over the breakfast table.

Her cheeks stung as she approached a large wardrobe that almost reached to the ceiling, with carved doors that opened on well-oiled hinges though it was a piece of furniture that must have been well over a century old. It was cavernous inside and as Arabel had half expected, it was well stocked with clothes for all occasions . . . a woman's clothes.

She hesitated and then drew out a soft gold dress and held it against her . . . yes, it was obviously the same size as the dress she was wearing and too costly to have ever been bought with a secretarial wage. The Don, her husband, had had the wardrobe stocked out for her . . . dresses, wraps, coats, shoes, there they were in generous abundance, the gifts of a man who once again had achieved a certain purpose, to have for his wife a woman fair and strange and unlike all those others he had known as a bullfighter.

That was what he must have decided when he first met her, and fate had conspired to assist him in his purpose . . . he had what he wanted while Arabel's desires were lost in the mists of amnesia, perhaps lost to her for always in the depths of some prison cell.

Was there anything here in the wardrobe that belonged to her past life and which might help her to remember? She searched frantically, and recalled what the Don had said about going to her apartment to fetch some of her belongings before they had boarded the plane. Ah—she drew out a fawn-coloured trouser suit and studied it. The material was nice but obviously less expensive than that of the other things, and with a shaking hand she searched the pockets of the tunic, but found only a white handkerchief embroidered in the corner with a tiny gold flower.

A fleur-de-lys, and when she raised the cambric to her nose she breathed a scent that was faintly spicy, as if she had bought it in a Latin market-place where she might have wandered during her lunch breaks from the office where she had worked.

She breathed deeply of the scent and fought to break through the caul over her mind, but there was nothing tangible to cling to, only the painful feeling that somewhere she had fallen in love, dramatically and probably for the first time in her life, and that the trauma of it had led inevitably to her present predicament.

The Doña Arabel Ildefonso de la Dura, with everything a woman might wish for, except the one thing that mattered most of all . . . the man she really cared for!

It was then that she decided to put on the trouser suit, something she had bought with her own money and which had nothing to do with Don Cortez. She unzipped the flowered chiffon, so delicate and fine that when removed it weighed hardly anything in her hand. His choice, that she be seen in things ultra-feminine and appealing to his ultra-maleness. She felt tempted to toss the dress carelessly aside, but something restrained her, perhaps some remnant of training from her charity childhood, that everything cost money and wastefulness was a sin. She hung the chiffon on the hanger from which she had taken the trouser suit and placed it in the wardrobe. She stood there slim and soft-skinned in her lacy slip, feeling the beat of her heart as she put on the outfit that was associated with her former life.

In this suit would she meet his family, knowing in advance that her action would displease him; feeling some sense of revenge because he wouldn't give her time in which to become accustomed to his face, his ways . . . his passions.

She smoothed the tunic over her hips and returned to the mirror to twirl her hair into a smooth knot at the nape of her neck, fixing it with pins from a little chiselled glass bowl on the dressing-table. Now she looked more capable and less defenceless, and she also noticed how the classic style revealed the shadows under her cheekbones, and in her blue eyes.

Her heart knew, even if her mind refused admittance of the truth, that she was a woman who had suffered a painful emotional experience which had somehow led to her arrest in Venezuela. That had merely paved the way for Don Cortez to remove her forcibly from the man whom she really loved. She felt sure of it. He had seen a way to get her, and with all the ruthless daring of the *espada* he had carried through his plan and brought her to San Devilla as his bride.

She stood there and looked into her own frightened eyes and felt like the bride of the devil himself!

CHAPTER FIVE

MERIENDA, a charming Spanish word for tea, would be served at four o'clock, her husband had said, and Arabel was anxious to go downstairs rather than risk having him come to the bedroom again.

She walked along the gallery with its mosaic walls that felt cool to the touch as she made her way down the stairs, trailing her fingers along the curving balustrade. There in the long hall she stood hesitant until she caught the sound of music being played in one of the rooms. Arabel followed the sound and found herself in front of the door from which it emerged; an arching door of beautifully meshed iron that gave her a view into the room.

A young girl was inside and she was performing some kind of a Spanish dance to the fiery rhythm of the music, young arms making graceful motions about her shining dark head.

Arabel thought instantly that this must be one of the Don's youthful cousins, and she surely looked too pretty to offer the kind of hostility that Arabel dreaded. She stood looking through the meshed iron at the dancing figure . . . her husband had said that he had never known his father, therefore the relatives he had living with him at the ranch had to be those on his mother's side. An aunt and her children who were made welcome here because he could well afford to keep them, for being so very Spanish he wouldn't wish to debase his sense of honour by not sharing his good fortune with those of his blood.

How would they react to his very new wife? Would they be affronted that he had chosen to marry a foreigner instead of bringing into the family circle a woman of their own culture; a woman reared to the belief that men were the masters who must be won over with charm and flattery, and Latin *sal.*

The girl's dress whirled around her, petalled with crimson polka-dots and cinched in against her slender waist. Her fingers clicked and her eyes sparkled, and inborn in her was the Iberian grace of the deep south. Even when she noticed Arabel through the iron imagery of the *sala* door she didn't lose her poise but came gradually to a stillness that was almost that of an odalisque.

Oriental-shaped eyes gazed into Arabel's. 'So!' The girl seemed almost to hiss the word. 'You are the one!'

Arabel's heart sank, and then the girl flung open the door between them and a lively curiosity came into her eyes as they swept the Don's bride from head to heel. The girl had a smooth gold skin and her face was a perfect oval, with tiny kiss-curls on her cheeks. Everything about her seemed young and pampered, with in the curve of her lips a promise of adult sensuousness.

'You are dressed like a *jovencito*.' The girl gave a faintly mocking but unspiteful laugh. 'I would never wear trousers to hide my legs, but I understand that the foreign woman is different—or have you ugly legs and don't wish Cortez to notice them?'

'He's noticed them!' The words came from Arabel almost before she realised, and she instantly knew that she was on the defensive with the Don's family and the natural curiosity they would have about her. At her reply the girl gave a laugh, reached out a hand and drew Arabel into the *sala*.

'It is just a fashion, eh? Me, I don't like it. I am a woman and happy to be that way, for life can be harder on men who have to do the providing, and sometimes like Cortez risk their lives in order to make something of life.'

Arabel was drawn to the centre of the room and there she was pertly gazed upon by this extremely self-assured Spanish girl.

'Cortez,' she added, 'had to make his own glory and couldn't be dependent upon his ancestors—ah, you flinch when I say that. You don't like it that he was a famous matador?'

'I'm glad at least that he no longer makes his living that way.' Arabel spoke tensely and glanced about the *sala* and up at the ceiling, scalloped like shells from which hung a pair of wrought-gold chandeliers. Against the pearly-pale walls were a pair of mosaic pictures, one of the Madonna and the other of an eagle-knight.

'Why, because he would be risking his life, or putting a sword into a bull?'

Arabel looked at the girl and decided to be quite honest. 'I can't pretend to be enamoured of the bull-fight. It goes against all my principles and seems horribly cruel.'

'A man has to be brave to do it.'

'Or barbaric.'

The slanting dark eyes narrowed and the girl placed her hands against her hips in a faintly insolent attitude. 'So, cruelty and piety go hand in hand in our country, but at least we repent of our sins and don't pretend there is no hell to burn in. I believe the Americanos live only for pleasure and don't count the cost?'

'That isn't altogether true,' Arabel protested. 'I daresay in every country there are the pious and the pleasure-seekers. Spain isn't a land of saints!'

'But it is a land where the man is the master.' The girl said it a trifle tauntingly, as if already her family had decided that the American wife of Don Cortez was going to rebel against the domination of her Spanish husband. Arabel glanced downwards and saw soft puma skins spread across the polished floor, a tawny-gold in colour that made her hands clench at her sides. And there to the left of her, in a cabinet of carved richness, was an open case of steel swords with cross-shaped hilts, and hanging beside the weapons were fighting capes of a peacock splendour, torn here and there and with faded red splashes on them. Her nostrils tautened and she breathed the scent of watered stone from the enclosed patio beyond the *sala* windows that lay open like doors.

The music of the *Ritual Fire Dance* had died away and Arabel was intensely aware of her own vulnerable strangeness in this household that saw glory in steel that had killed and in capes that were marked by the blood of the Don.

'Bah!' The girl clicked her fingers in a Latin gesture of scorn. 'Would you want a *maricón* for a husband?'

'A what?' Arabel looked puzzled.

'A pansy boy, one who would be like a sister to you, combing your hair and wearing your scent.'

'That's a bit of an extreme example.' Arabel had to smile, albeit nervously, as she saw in her mind the careless animal swagger of the Don, and the strongly marked features of a passionate male.

'Why are you so on edge?' The girl eyed her with curiosity. 'Cortez is a very prominent man and a girl of these parts would be wild with delight had he chosen to make her his wife. He is very manly, strong in character, and he has *sal* as well as authority. What is wrong with you that you stand there with a face like milk, looking as if your knees are going to give way? Are you nervous of us?'

'I—I suppose I am.' Even as Arabel spoke she wondered if the Don had told his people that she had just come from hospital and was suffering from amnesia. Surely he had not left her to pretend that there was nothing wrong? Surely he must know that they'd be inquisitive about her and ask all sorts of questions!

'You think we won't like you?' The ripe young lips curled into a smile. 'Mamita probably won't, as she is in her very bones a woman of Andalusia who firmly believes that like should marry like, and you are about as much like a southern girl as a lily is to a carnation. You find me very candid, eh?'

Arabel nodded and in her turn wanted to be candid; she wanted to say that she was married to a man who seemed a total stranger to her. That she had no recollection of her own wedding, and felt every kind of fear of the future. It was that little twinge of fear that kept her from blurting out the truth; first of all she had to know from him why he had chosen to pretend that everything was normal between them. Did he think that it would add to his family distrust of a foreign bride if they also knew that she came to San Devilla in a state of confusion and mental shock?

'Spanish people believe that secrets in a family can cause trouble.' His young cousin gave a toss of her head so the small rings in her ears caught the sunlight that came through the trees beyond the *sala* windows, then like a young cat she gave a sudden pounce and caught Arabel by the wrist. 'This is your betrothal bracelet, eh? How very romantic, blue like your eyes. What did you give Cortez?'

'I—we didn't have time for any shopping. We left Venezuela almost as soon as the wedding ceremony was over.' This was hellish, not knowing how much to reveal and how much to conceal. 'He probably didn't expect anything.'

'Being content to have possession of his bride, eh?' Then the dark eyes narrowed and the slim fingers tightened on Arabel's wrist, pressing the sapphires against her skin. 'You have had no honeymoon? No *luna de mielo,* as we call it! But we understood you were in Cordoba for a week?'

'I—I wasn't terribly well—some bug I picked up, no doubt.' Arabel felt awful about lying, and at the same time slightly petrified in case she said the wrong thing and made things worse than they already were between herself and Don Cortez. Why couldn't he tell them the real facts? Did he suppose his relations would think her *loca* if he revealed to them that her mind was a blank where he was concerned, and that she felt not the faintest affection for him? Did his pride have to come before her pain?

'Yes,' drawled the girl, 'it is *manifestado* that you are still very shy with regard to Cortez. I thought there had to be some reason for that look about you, like a scared heifer edging its way into the ring and ready to scramble over anything in order to avoid the entanglement of the cape—the heifers are not killed, you understand, but are tested by the boys to see if they will become mothers of brave bulls. Is Cortez testing you in that way, I wonder? It would be like him.'

The girl laughed and swung Arabel's wrist so that the blue gems sparkled. 'He obviously thinks you are worth something, eh? This bracelet must have cost a pretty penny, and men who have worked and faced danger for their money don't throw it around. Is he madly enamoured of you?'

'I don't want to talk about it.' Arabel dragged her wrist from the girl's fingers and went to stand by the open windows, where she took deep breaths of the tangy air and prayed that her husband would walk in and put an end to this minor inquisition. She didn't want to be openly rude to his young cousin, but she was beginning to feel baited and in her present state of mind it was less than bearable.

'We say that those who want to break open the pomegranate so all the seeds can be counted are only playing at love.' The young face grew quieter and more serious. 'I am Luz, and I hope that somewhere a man is waiting for me to return among his ribs.'

Arabel swung round and stared at the girl, amazed by what she had said, struck by its biblical quality and how it expressed the belief of these people that a woman was the rib of the man she married.

'Aren't you the rib of Cortez?'

'It sounds—primitive.'

'We are primitive in some things. Our emotions can be very intense—*sal española* it is called, warmth of soul as well as body.'

'It seems a lot to live up to.' Arabel let her shadowed eyes wander around this very Spanish room and her gaze fell again on the display of swords and fighting capes. These people were deep ... deeper than she had realised, with their roots not fully broken away from the cults of the Moorish occupation. A woman's place was to please the man who wished to live with her, and God help her if those of his blood suspected that she was a sword in his side instead of a rib.

'Perhaps you are a honey-bee who has landed among wasps,' Luz drawled. 'Time will tell, and it won't do, Americano girl, if you have married Cortez for just his money.'

'It wasn't that,' Arabel said quietly. 'You can take my word for it.'

'I want to take your word, for Cortez has been good to us, and his woman had better be good to him.'

'That sounds like a threat.' Arabel forced a smile to her lips. 'I hope it isn't, Luz. I hope we can be friends.'

Luz shrugged. 'I am glad that my cousin has married, if only for one thing, that we shall have a baby in the family and a big celebration when he is baptised—how you blush! Aren't these matters mentioned in the households of the Americanos?'

'I expect so, but your cousin and I are only just married and it could be some time before we make it possible for you to enjoy such a celebration.'

'It will happen.' Luz spoke confidently. 'Cortez makes no secret of wanting a son, and you are desirable enough for his purpose. Matadors are unlike other men, you know. They live furiously and die by bits each time they enter the arena. The arms of women are their consolation, but not good women, you understand? Not the kind a man would marry, for no real Spaniard would become the husband of a woman who had not kept her virtue. He would feel cheated if he found that his bride was not immaculate and in his terrible temper he would throw her out on the street, perhaps through the bedroom window.'

'It seems to be in the Spanish temperament to go to extremes.' Arabel couldn't suppress a slight smile at the emotional pride and passion of this girl, in whom it was easy to detect the blood of Don Cortez. 'So a woman has to be more or less a nun until she marries, but it's permissible for a man to have a wicked temper?'

'Spaniards are fierce and possessive, but this is much better than for a man to be calm and boring. And even if a girl does have to be virtuous, there is nothing to stop her from practising *gracia*.'

'And what is that?' Arabel couldn't help being interested, and when all was said and done she had to learn the ways of these people for there was little hope of unbinding herself from the iron chains of Spanish marriage.

'*Gracia* is greater than beauty,' said Luz, her eyes slipping over Arabel's face. 'It is a melting charm that can hold a man to a woman even as the years slip away and her youthful attractions don't melt but grow in pounds. But you are *norteamericana*. Do your sort stay slender, or do you grow stout in the middle years?'

'I expect everyone loses in time the first fine bloom of youth,' Arabel said drily. 'Aren't you a little young to be thinking so far ahead?'

'I am almost eighteen. And you, how old are you?'

'I'm twenty-two,' said Arabel, but the awful part was that she wasn't really sure of her age. She looked and felt about that age, but try as she might she couldn't recall a thing about herself that was definite. It was as if she had been born in that Cordoban hospital and by some magic formula had attained the status of adult without any of the growing pains. Here she was, a stranger's wife transported into a strange world, related by a slip of paper and a pair of rings to a clan that was proud and not easily won over by someone from outside their range of experiences. There would be suspicion only thinly concealed beneath the Latin courtesy. There would be a certain jealousy, for the Don's aunt and cousins were accustomed to being the centre of his life, and from now on his wife would absorb a good deal of his attention.

'Our men take parenthood for granted,' said Luz, and a flash of challenge came into her dark eyes. 'You are going to give the matador a son or two for him to teach the old tricks?'

'We shall see.' Arabel was more disturbed by this trend to the conversation than she cared to show; it reminded her too forcibly of that scene in the *camera sposa*, swept over her once again that sense of helplessness, and the shock of horror when she had dragged the black patch from that eyeless cavity in his lean face. There was no escaping the fact that she was the wife of Ildefonso and she would be made to live up to that role by all of those who resided at the *estancia.* In the first place he had been good to them, and secondly she would be watched as if by hawks for being less than a Spanish bride.

'Don't look so worried.' Luz gave a light laugh and clicked her fingers. 'All women are made for three things; love, pain and pleasure.'

With these words she moved out into the patio with her natural grace, almost as if she were in tune with invisible guitar players who made music for her alone. Arabel followed and breathed the scent of a lovely flowering tree that shaded the patio table; a scent that combined nutmeg and lemons, added to which was the aroma of peaches, for at one side the walls were rampant with the espaliered fruits that hung among the green leaves like globes of eatable gold. There were also clouds of golden creeper and the creamy-blue contrast of plumbago. Pink and ruby myrtles, amaryllis and columbines, and the *maracuja* so strangely like the hammer and nails of the Passion of Christ.

Arabel didn't question why she knew these flowers; some instinct told her that she had seen their like in that other Latin country in which she had lived and worked. These odds and ends of knowledge seemed to grow around the blankness of her inner mind in the most annoying fashion, like thorns that wouldn't let her through to come face to face with herself.

'You frown,' said Luz, who was standing against a frame of flowers like soft pale bells. 'Don't you find agreeable the ambiance of San Devilla? It was very much run down when Cortez first acquired it, but he has put money and imagination into the property and made of it what every matador dreams of when he walks into the arena to the cheers of a crowd who wait hopefully for the horn thrust should he prove less cunning than the angry bull.'

'There undoubtedly was an occasion when he lost his cunning,' said Arabel, and even as she spoke she felt again a grinding sensation deep inside her and envisaged yet again what lay behind the triangle of black velvet that Don Cortez wore.

'Even so,' Luz gave a proud toss of her head, and her eyes flashed sparks at the Nordic girl who had invaded her Andalusian world, 'Cortez still took the bull! I heard it from someone who was there—with blood on his face like a scarlet mask Cortez returned steel for the horn. Someone screamed in the crowd, and then came the cheers as the bull fell at the feet of my cousin. You don't meet his sort every day ... nor do you marry him!'

Luz looked Arabel up and down, scorn in her eyes. 'He must have been blinded by your blue eyes when he chose you for his wife. He'll regret it, for in Spanish people there is an affinity that outsiders never understand, and you are a rank outsider with your milky skin and your hair that pretends to be gold. How often do you have to dye it in order to stop the dark roots from showing? Ugh! There is nothing more unattractive than to see blonde hair with roots the colour of tarnished copper!'

A positive indignation swept over Arabel as the Spanish girl flung the insulting words at her. 'My hair isn't dyed,' she said, sparks of temper in her own eyes. 'You're a spiteful little cat, aren't you, and out to make me feel as unwelcome as possible. Well, don't forget that I'm the Don's wife, and that he might not like it if I have to put up with insults from jealous adolescents.'

'Jealous?' The girl's hands curled into hooks at the sides of her dress. 'Of you?'

'Yes.' For the first time since coming here Arabel felt sure of something. 'You've made quite a hero of my husband and you can't bear it that he has brought home a wife. You'll have to get used to it, Luz, for he assures me that I'm staying here.'

'Even though you don't really want to stay?' It was a shot in the dark, and even Luz couldn't have been prepared for the instant distress that showed on Arabel's face. She was unable to hide the trepidation that she felt in being here among total strangers; the strength left her legs and she sank down on one of the patio chairs and stared blindly at the flower-covered walls and the graceful wrought iron that enclosed the *estancia* from the rest of the world.

'Has he forced you into marrying him?' Luz drew nearer to Arabel, an avid curiosity in her eyes. 'Are you one of those girls I have heard about—reluctant to be a wife; afraid of a man because he is so much stronger and can force his will upon a woman? How strange to be like that. Most of the girls I know are waiting for the day when a man comes to her grille and makes fire with his eyes. Ah, is it true what they say about women of the north—that they are cold and independent and don't care for men to be their masters? Then no wonder you sit there with a face like white jasmine.'

Luz gave a mocking laugh and reached out to touch the gold of Arabel's hair. 'He'll own you, foreign woman, from your hair to your small toes.'

Arabel jerked away from the girl's touch. Primitive words from the lips of someone who shared the same bloodstream as Don Cortez ... words whose truth and threat seemed to stab into Arabel like so many tiny barbs, making her body tingle with undreamed-of terrors from which she wanted to run, except that this patio was circular like an arena, and the eyes of

Luz were like those of the Spanish women who watched the bullfight and flung their carnations to the matador in his shining suit of lights, the great cloak like a flame of gold and scarlet licking around his lean hard body, hiding from his prey the sword with its shaft of pure steel.

'You shivering ice woman!' Luz hissed the words as she leaned down to Arabel, breathing them into her ear. 'You should be married to one of your own sort, not to someone like Cortez. Or perhaps you shouldn't be married at all if you expect a man to treat you like a nun.'

'You can take it from me, Luz, that my wife doesn't expect anything of the sort.'

At the sound of that deep masculine voice Arabel's heart seemed to check for a second, and she told herself wildly that she couldn't look at him and not feel again that awful urge to scream. But with long silent strides he had come to her side and the next moment was standing between her and his young cousin. Compelled against her will, Arabel looked up at him and met that single eye that could hold a dozen different expressions when he looked at her, dominant, possessive, demanding that she act the proper wife in front of his relatives.

'Getting to know each other?' he drawled, and he stood there with a hand on the back of Arabel's chair and he looked more of a spaniard than ever, for he had changed and wore a *guayavera*, a shirt that was styled to the very shape and skin of the Andalusian male. His trousers were tight-waisted and seemed to emphasise his lean hardness of build. He glanced around the walled patio and his nostrils tensed as he drew into himself the many combined scents of the plants and the peaches. 'It feels good to be home and I don't think I shall be travelling again for a while—

how have you been, Luz? Has everyone kept well and busy in my absence?'

The young cousin moved towards him and her dark eyes were fixed upon his face. She reached out with her expressive hands and closed them on his shoulders, and Arabel could see that she was pressing her fingertips deep into the muscles under that fine white shirt.

'Why have you married a foreigner?' Luz demanded of him. 'This girl is like one of your golden veiled fish and if she doesn't watch out we shall swallow her like those carp you removed from the pool. Are we to receive the same treatment, cousin? We of your blood, are we to take second place to this woman?'

'What an over-active imagination you have, Luz!' He gave a laugh, but it was brief and hard. 'First you wish to know if Arabel expects to be treated like a nun, now you ask if I shall turn out my family from the *estancia* in order to make room for one slim young woman. Or are you threatening, little cousin, to take nips out of my golden wife?'

Luz gazed up into his face, searching his features as if his marriage made him suddenly a stranger to her. 'You do look a little different, Cortez, as I have heard that marriage makes a man. You seem more aloof, as if now there are secrets in your heart that you cannot share with us.'

He shrugged his shoulders and glanced, meaningly, at Arabel. 'When you find someone whom you wish to marry then you will understand, Luz, that a man and his wife do share a very special kind of relationship. It was inevitable that I should marry. You all knew that. It cannot have come as a total surprise, and I certainly hope that it hasn't come as an unpleasant one?'

Luz swept her eyes over Arabel. 'If she were a Spanish girl——'

'Well, she isn't,' he cut in. 'I marry who pleases me, and if you aren't careful, my girl, I shall exert my authority and find for you a husband who will keep you in order. You grow pert and think that your pretty face will excuse you from censure; but be careful, Luz, I am head of this house and Arabel is now mistress of it and I won't tolerate any of your impertinence with regard to her. She has been not too well and has rather shaky nerves at present.'

'Has she?' Luz stood there with her hands on those hard, strong shoulders, and then with a smile she leaned forward and trailed her red lips against his cheek. 'A nervous woman for Ildefonso—who would have thought it?'

'I care not a snap of the fingers what anyone thinks.' He put the girl away from him. 'Where is your mother? She is coming down for *merienda*, eh? She is not taking the attitude that I have turned the world upside down because I have taken an American bride?'

'I am here now, Cortez, son of my sister, so don't start letting loose that famous temper of yours.' The woman who spoke came across the patio on the arm of a slim young man with an unmistakable resemblance to Luz; she wore grey silk patterned with small silver lilies, and there was a square of black lace over her grey-streaked dark hair, fastened by a sparkling brooch. She was a small woman, but she obviously had authority, for there was a subtle change in Don Cortez's manner as he took one of his aunt's hands and kissed the back of it. He assisted her into a high-backed cane chair, while her son stood by and stared at Arabel.

Once settled the aunt also studied her nephew's

wife, and it was all Arabel could do to sit there and be under observation by those unsparing Spanish eyes. She fought to remain seated while with every atom of her body she longed to leap up from her chair and to run away from these strangers who had every right to be suspicious of her ... the Don's wife and yet an intruder into their lives.

CHAPTER SIX

'So, nephew, you are now a married man.' His aunt kept her gaze fixed upon Arabel as she spoke, and with a sudden adroit movement of her wrist she flicked open a black fan patterned with lacy butterflies. There could have been something significant in the gesture, for Arabel seemed to know there was a language of the fan that Spanish women were adept at expressing. She felt the lean body of her husband go as taut as one of those steel swords he had used in the bullring and she didn't need to look at him to see that his brows had merged into a black line.

'Yes, *amita,*' he replied. 'I am a fortunate man.'

'Is that really so?' Scepticism lay deep in the aunt's eyes as they probed Arabel. 'I daresay the Arab in you likes the fair skin, eh?'

'I have never denied, *amita*, my affinity with our ancestors.' As he spoke he turned to the manservant who had appeared on the patio with a tray of drinks. 'Ah, I have been longing for my pisco sour! You will join me, Juan, while the ladies take fruit juice?'

'I will not have my son hardened to the drinking habit,' snapped his aunt. 'You would teach him all your habits—the good *Dios* help the son that you will have—and he will no more acquire a taste for that strong drink than he will accept the *alternativa* as you would like. Juan is going to be an architect, not a fighter of bulls. He is going to keep his looks and not lose them to the horn of a bull!'

'I salute you for being a careful mother.' A wicked little smile came into the Don's eye as he raised his glass to his lips, the liquid a pale shimmering green in the sunlight.

Arabel could feel the tremor in her wrist as she accepted a glass of tangerine juice and watched with tormented eyes the way her husband drank his pisco sour in almost a single gulp. Was it possible that he was as nervous as she? Oh, it was ludicrous to suppose such a thing, and she glanced away from him and watched the various dishes being placed on the cane table, anchovy-stuffed olives, crab meat and prawns, and cakes of a melting sweetness. Luz sat down and began to eat with the careless greed of a girl whose emotions were not yet deeply troubled. She enjoyed drama, Arabel thought, as she relished the rhythm of the Andalusian flamenco.

Juan came to the table and sat down, and he gave Arabel a rather shy smile as he took a plate and put food on it. 'You are eating, *señora*?' he asked. 'The crab is very nice, and look how big are these prawns. May I serve you with something?'

'I—I'm not really hungry,' she gave him a hesitant smile. 'You go ahead and eat.'

'Is she finicky?' the aunt asked of Don Cortez. 'She does realise that in this house we eat Spanish food and not all that wrapped and frozen stuff that Americans are fond of?'

'We had lunch on the way here,' he explained. 'I am sure Arabel will eat a good dinner later on this evening, though I would beg of you, *amita*, not to try and stuff her like a lamb for the next *fiesta*. I like her the way she is.'

'Skin and bone,' snapped his aunt, 'like most of these foreign women. They have headaches upon the slightest whim, and make of having a *pequeño* the big trouble and expense, with feeding from a bottle in place of the natural source.'

'For heaven's sake,' he gave a brief laugh, 'Arabel will suppose that she is here to join the livestock instead of the household if you go on in that manner! Take no notice, *mi esposa*, of my good aunt. I have remained a bachelor for so long that she has to get used to the idea that I am now married and likely to take exception to her remarks about my wife.' As he spoke he moved his hand until it was resting lightly over Arabel's shoulder, the warmth of his fingers striking through the material of her tunic. She had to fight not to pull away from his touch, a very definite hint to his family that she belonged to him and they had better not vent too openly their disappointment that he had not taken a Spanish bride.

'It might interest you to know, *amita*,' he said, deliberately, 'that I regard Arabel as very lovely to look upon, and that it doesn't worry me in the least that she hasn't the wide hips of a cow, nor the long black mane of an amorous mare. You take my meaning, I hope? She is *my* woman, and I don't want her frightened by any suggestion that she is to provide me with an heir to my glorious name as soon as possible.'

'As you say, Cortez.' His aunt took a sip of her sherry, and gestured at Luz to place a slice of marzipan cake on a plate for her. 'Charming blossom is not always an assurance, anyway, that the fruit will be sweet.'

'Sweet enough for my strong teeth,' he rejoined, and taking a switch-bladed knife from his pocket he approached the peach espalier and cut from it several of the luscious-looking fruits. He brought them to the table and placed a couple in front of Arabel. 'Try these for sweetness,' he said to her.

Luz reached greedily for a peach and sank her teeth into it, a bracelet jangling with charms against the golden skin of her arm. Love knots, lanterns, and the crescent ... claw of the lover. Arabel could only wonder what it felt like to be so uninhibited, so sure of who you were that nothing mattered except that a certain man found you attractive.

'Allow me,' said Juan, and with his own knife he sliced a peach for Arabel and removed the stone. He glanced up at Cortez, boyish and a trifle defiant. 'Do you mind, cousin? Your wife is so reserved.'

'Of course she is.' Cortez looked mocking, standing there in the sunlight, wholly brown-skinned except for the bone whiteness of his knuckles as he gripped his second glass of pisco sour. Against a background of graceful myrtles and creamy-blue plumbago, hiding the solid stone of the *estancia* walls, Arabel saw the Arab in her husband ... the wild, barely tamed heart and the depth of power and passion. 'In every way my opposite. So what?' He challenged all of them as he stood there, and only his aunt had the temerity of age to answer him. 'Oil and water, nephew, have never been known to mix, but I've no doubt that you have the arrogance to defy the laws of chemistry. Also you have been an *espada* too long to set aside the cape and sword entirely.'

'Meaning?'

Cortez looked at his aunt with a sardonic lifting of his black eyebrow, and in that moment Arabel seemed to see him as he must often have looked when he strode into the arena to face the lunging horns of the bull.

'A man who has tasted danger would choke on honey.' His aunt shot a shrewd look at Arabel. 'There has to be more to this one than meets the eye—tell me, girl, where did you meet this man?'

Arabel tensed, and then had to look at Cortez for guidance in her reply. What was she to say when he hadn't told his family that her memory of him began in hospital, and that beyond that moment there was only a blank in her mind, and a feeling deep inside her that if she had known him before the loss of her memory then it had been with antipathy, not with any kind of affection? She even felt as if she might have hated him, and if she had hated him he had shrugged it off and gone ahead with marrying her.

Cortez drained his glass and set it down carefully on the cane table. When he straightened again his face was set in firm lines, each feature as hard cast as if made of iron. A formidable face, as if he faced again the moment of truth. His hand moved against the side of his trousers and fingers clenched as if seeking the cross-handled hilt of his sword.

Arabel watched him and felt sure that he would make something up, but instead he told them what he had told her, that she had been dragged off to prison and he had married her there in order to get her released ...

'Arabel is still a little confused by her experience.' He shrugged his shoulders. 'You must make allowances if she seems—distraite.'

'How ghastly!' Luz was staring from her cousin to his wife, Latin male and Nordic woman, a striking contrast to each other. 'I've heard of girls and women being raped in those places!'

'Luz!' Her mother looked shocked. 'Your mouth should be washed out!'

'Well, so they have——' Luz stared at Arabel.

'Were you frightened out of your mind?'

'She was.' He spoke curtly. 'Now you all know of this, you will forget it and allow Arabel to find her nerves again. She has been through a bad experience, but here at the *estancia* she will recover and learn to be—happy.'

When he said that Arabel looked up at him and she wondered if his optimism was as cynical as her own. He knew exactly how she had felt about him, but she could only make a guess. He knew, but he wanted her and that would overcome any scruples he might feel about keeping her here.

As useless to beg mercy of Don Cortez as any of the bulls whose hearts he had stopped with an expert thrust of shining steel.

'Come.' He leaned over her and his fingers took her lightly by the chin. 'You must eat something, for like Arabs we regard the sharing of food as a sign of trust—and you must learn to trust us.'

'You must give me time to learn,' she said, and she knew what lay in her eyes, the wild hope that he would be generous enough to treat her like a guest—if only for a little while, and allow her to adjust to the strangeness of her surroundings; to establish some link with all she had forgotten.

But would he be that kind when he knew that the return of her memory would reawaken those loveless feelings which she had felt for him? Once he truly possessed her it would be harder to find a way out of this marriage of convenience.

'You have all the time in the world,' he said, a trifle arrogantly. 'Time is not the master in Spain.'

'Man is the master, I suppose?' She looked directly into his face, and felt close to her the aliveness and vitality in that javelin-like body, running molten under the skin that made her own seem so startling in its whiteness. In swift mental pictures she saw herself gathered close to that warm, dark-haired chest, and she almost felt those firmly carved lips travelling over her. A painful little quiver shot its way through her, and the next moment she was on her feet and running away from him, across the patio, anywhere, entangling herself in veils of heady jasmine near a Moorish fountain, and then finding a little iron gate that opened to her hand to let her into another area of this rambling estate.

She ran, knowing full well that he followed, until the hopelessness of running brought her up short against the scaly trunk of a palm tree, her slim body crushing the bougainvillaea that grew around its base.

A shudder swept through her as his hands closed on her waist and he swung her round and pulled her against the hard warmth of his shoulder. 'There is nowhere for you but here—here with me.' He spoke with a clipped finality. 'Face it, *querida*, you are penniless, dependent, and at a loss to know yourself and what it is that you truly want. You must let me do the thinking for you. You must allow me to know what is best for my wife.'

'Would I be your wife if the circumstances had been different?' She flung back her head and demanded to be told the truth. 'Would I ever have found myself married to you—if I hadn't been in the kind of trouble you took advantage of?'

'No.' He said it without any hesitancy. 'I had explicit reason to know that you would never have married me—willingly.'

'Meaning that I—I had no time for you, isn't that the truth?'

'Perhaps.' He shrugged, but the sun seemed to bite deeper into the lines of his lean face, shadowed by that dark patch where he was disfigured. 'But that is in the past and nothing alters the fact that you are here at San Devilla and that Spanish law makes you wholly mine. I have no conscience about it. You heard what Luz said a while ago, to the shock of her mother, and it could well have happened had I not interceded on your behalf. Tell me,' he lifted her face to his, holding his hand around her throat, his fingers spread dark and warm against her silky skin and her pounding pulse, 'would you sooner they did it than I?'

She shuddered and stared at the almost iron firmness of his chin and jawbone, and in contrast the hint of sensuality in the full curving of his lower lip. Suddenly that sensuality seemed to make a subtle alteration in the hard contours of his face, and with a sudden intake of breath he bent his head and laid his lips against her throat.

'Sweet,' he muttered. 'Sweet as lilies—do you think I could leave you in their dirty clutches? I knew you'd hate me! I knew that as sure as I knew hell, but I don't care a damn! I have you! I hold you! I'll make you want me even if you refuse to love me!'

'I'll never—never want you.' Her hands struck at him, and then were almost bent back at the wrist as he drew her harshly close to him and silenced her mouth with his own. His kiss struck deep, deep down inside her, twisting the nerves as if on a rack, making her sag at the knees so that she was pushed in support against the tree until he had finished with her.

She leaned there, breath and hope crushed out of her, dizzy from his kiss and the heady scent of the flowers in the hot sun, and only her eyes seemed alive as they blazed like blue flames into his.

'I hate you!' she panted. 'I sensed it all along how I felt about you—arrogant, cruel, out to get your own way because being a winner means more than being a loser. It's bred in your bone! You love it when you can plunge your sword up to the hilt into a maddened creature! Your aunt is right—it's what you live for, and settling down to be a landowner isn't going to satisfy you, so you bring me here to torment!'

'That is what you really believe?' he demanded, and his face seemed all hard bone as he spoke, and his lips had thinned to a knife-edge. 'That is what you take me for, a baiting brute who wishes to see you cowed and whimpering, with all the Nordic pride beaten out of you, to become a mere doormat for me to wipe my feet on? You believe that is what a Spanish husband is? If so, *mi alma*, then you have much to learn, and the sooner the tutorial begins the better for both of us!'

'No doubt the better for you,' she flung back in his angry face. 'And stop calling me *your soul*—you have about as much soul as a vulture! You found I wasn't to be had when I had my full faculty of mind, but you soon swooped on the leavings when they dragged me off to that prison. In front of your relatives you make yourself sound a real heroic figure who came to the rescue of the damsel in distress, but you just wanted some kind of revenge on me for giving you the cold eye before I landed myself in prison. It must have been like a barb in your skin to meet a woman who didn't give a damn that you had been a dashing bullfighter, and who was merely disgusted by your way of life. Deny it if you can, Don Cortez! I was disgusted, wasn't I?'

'Horrified,' he drawled. 'You revealed in no uncertain manner that you hated the blood on the sand.'

'There!' Arabel felt curiously triumphant, for her instinct about their relationship had been the correct one and this surely meant that she couldn't be far removed from a complete recovery of her memory.

'I knew from the moment we met in that hospital that I would never have married you had I been in my right mind! I was forced into it and I—I believe I have this amnesia because I wanted to blot out what you had made me do. You made me, didn't you? I didn't speak those marriage vows very willingly, did I?'

Her eyes demanded and accused, densely blue in her otherwise white and tormented face. He gazed down at her and she could feel his bruising grip on her arms, holding her there against the massive palm tree, the shadows of the tendrilled leaves making his face more than ever that of a desert throwback. Tarik the one-eyed. Lean avenger with a sun-scorched skin, in whose hand the sword had been pitiless.

'I didn't wring them from your throat,' he said, half-mockingly. 'We stood together in the prison chapel, the shadows of the candle flames against the walls, the robes of the priest as pale as your face. The guards were there, watching like inquisitors. Will you say that I was Torquemada rather than they?'

His words were graphic, etching for her a black and white picture of that strange ceremony.

'That night, Arabel, you might have married the devil himself in order to get away from that place.'

'Perhaps I did marry him,' she rejoined. 'Surely only a devil would have had the gall to stand up to people like that.'

'Perhaps so.' A smile of pure irony lifted the corner of his lip. 'The ritual act of the bullfight is deep in the blood of Latin people, and perhaps it takes a devil to perform that ritual for them. Hundreds of times have I performed it, and that was why I was allowed to snatch a bone from those dogs. So, *querida*, you have something of the bullfight to be grateful for, and don't you deny that you would sooner be here at San Devilla than locked away in a sunless cell.'

'Oh, I don't doubt, Don Cortez, that I must be grateful for being at your mercy rather than theirs.' Still she defied him, for what peace could she find here if when memory opened its floodgates she found she must drown in the remorse of having a lover lost to her in that sunless prison house? 'I'll admit that your prison is rather more attractive, but you'll have to accept it if I treat you just like any other gaoler.'

'At least a gaoler who will permit you the sun on your skin and good clothes on your body.' His eye flicked over her sardonically. 'Why are you wearing that garment when you have in your wardrobe dresses of far more attraction? Personally speaking I am not enamoured of pants on a woman.'

'I'm quite sure you aren't.' Arabel let the defiance flood into her eyes. 'You believe that only the male of the species should wear the trousers, yet surely in the days of your Moorish ancestry the harem inmates wore pants?'

'Filmy things that were enticing on the female form rather than mannish, like those tailored things you have on. In future, *querida*, you will gratify me by wearing the clothes I had specially made for you in Seville, in materials and colours that suit your fairness of skin and hair. You are no longer an American secretary working for your living in an office. You are the wife of Ildefonso and you will enact that role both day and night—do I make my meaning clear enough for you?'

'As crystal, *señor*.' She gave him a look which she hoped was full of contempt for his male arrogance. 'I am as much a prisoner of San Devilla as if I was still in that other gaol, and the clothes of your choosing are to be my uniform, and my obedience to your every whim my penance for not being smitten with your cruel face!'

'Gracias, mi esposa.' His hands became deliberately hurtful as he forced her body against his, so that she felt the hard bone and sinew of him, hip and thigh. His face looking down into hers was cruel in that moment, lean and black-shadowed by the brows and the patch; a face such as the medieval artists of Spain had painted into the canvases of their marauders of rich, ancient Inca cities: a face that would have been equally at home under the swathings of a Moorish headcloth. Holding her like this he must have felt the tumultuous beating of her heart, for a shade of wanton enjoyment crept into his smile.

'You're welcome to exactly what I think of you,' she said, fear and fury mingling in her cry. 'Whatever you get from me as a wife you'll have to take—I don't intend to give you anything of my own free will!'

'Not even your hatred?' he mocked. 'Come, surely you have plenty of that to give to the man who risked his own freedom on your behalf?'

'You risked nothing,' she said scornfully. 'You were well aware that you'd be welcomed as a fearless killer of bulls, and I daresay all it took to have me brought from a cell to the chapel was a few bottles of Spanish cognac and a few gory tales of your triumphs in the arenas. After all, what is a woman? Only a hank of hair and a body for a man to enjoy! Her feelings are second-rate compared to those of the lordly male! I can just see you, Don Cortez, handing round the cognac and laughing over me with those louts——'

'Stop it!' His voice, then, was like a bull-whip cracking, and Arabel flinched before she could stop herself. 'How dare you say such things! You know in your heart that they aren't true!'

'I know very little at the present time, *señor*, except what I feel in my bones. When you walked into the prison to claim me, it was just as if you were walking into another arena to cape a bull and thrust steel into its heart.'

'I saved you, you insolent little fool, from being treated like a *thing*. Do you quite understand? Did not that mere child Luz put it into plain language? Do you imagine that because you are an American citizen you would be immune from what those thugs do to the women who fall into their filthy hands? Do you regard *my* hands as being as vicious as theirs? Be careful how you answer me, Arabel, for I haven't the most tolerant temper in the world, and if I lose it with you——'

'Is that a threat or a promise?' she asked, too carried away by resentment of her enforced marriage to care if he broke her neck in his anger. 'Oh, really, do you think I'm so lost in the clouds that I don't realise why I helped those students and risked my own safety? I know—I feel it inside me—that I cared for someone! One of those young men, and you know it, don't you? You know which one! And I've got to live with you and endure the thought of what he might be suffering—the man I love!'

Her words rang out in the patio and for a burning moment even the birds seemed to fall silent in the trees as Don Cortez stared down into her passionate face. He seemed to stop breathing, and then a muscle twitched violently in his jaw. A flare of anger, grand and terrible, struck across his face with all the merciless force of the sun across the patio. Angry temper seethed in that single eye of his, his hands bruised her, and his body seethed with it.

'If I believed that I'd kill you!' He barely breathed the words, yet they had a deadly force that went right through Arabel, to her very spine, so that she tingled from head to foot. 'You are mine, do you hear me? Mine! In thought, word and deed. I married you, and Ildefonso never wanted to marry any other woman. You are my wife, and I won't have you thinking that any other man has any right to you. I tell you here and now that *I* am the only man in your life!'

'You can tell me anything you like,' she flung back at him. 'You can force me to do whatever you wish, but you can't get inside my head and totally dominate me—and you know it. You'd have to choke the breath out of me to stop me from believing that on the night you hurried me away from Venezuela as your wife, we left behind us the man I really wanted. We're both going to have to live with that, Don Cortez. It will be like the garotte for all three of us!'

He shook her, then, so that her hair sprang loose from its chignon and cascaded about her neck and fell in a wave across her forehead. He stared down at the strands of gold against her white skin, and with a sudden groan he buried his face against hers.

'I did what I had to do, Arabel. Hate me for it if you must, but I can't let you go—I won't let you go. I'll insist on this marriage whatever it does to both of us, and whatever our private battles I will also insist that you behave with the correct decorum in front of my good aunt and her children. They are the only real kin I have and they respect me.'

'They feel under obligation to you,' Arabel breathed, feeling the thrust of his facial bones against her skin and the warmth of him like a brand she could hardly endure without letting out a screaming demand that he let go of her, for now, at least.

'*Querida*, when did you learn to be cruel with words?' His breath was harsh and warm across her face. 'Ah, but such lovely hair, thick, puma-gold.

Cristos, I want you despite what you say to me!'

'You have me, haven't you?' she said coldly. 'For better or for worse.'

'Hellfire and damnation?' The irony was creeping back into his voice, and taking her hair in his fist he bound it around her throat as if to throttle her. 'A golden rope to choke you with, or a silken yashmak to hide the hating in your eyes. It was your hair I loved before anything else.'

'You—you don't love me!' she choked.

'Please yourself, *querida.*' He shrugged his lean, hard shoulders. 'You are mine to protect, mine to possess, whatever you choose to think. Our marriage was sanctioned by a priest of the Holy Roman church and you are mine through hell and fury—perhaps even a dash of heaven, my little spitfire.'

'Heaven?' Her eyes shot blue sparks into his. 'That will be the day, *señor hidalgo.*'

'Or the night,' he drawled meaningly.

CHAPTER SEVEN

THE tempo of emotion slowed down, the pulsating excitement died away, leaving Arabel weary and worn. She rested there against the palm tree and could hardly believe that with a sardonic inclination of his head Don Cortez had turned on his heel and sauntered away, every inch a son of southern Spain, holding himself as lithe and straight as a guardsman, with that suggestion of a cloak flowing from the firm shoulders.

Arabel sighed and pushed the tousled hair from her brow ... was it always going to be like this whenever they were alone? A battle of wills that roused her to a high pitch of nervous intensity and left her feeling as if he had swept his Spanish garden with her.

Something quivered in her throat and caught at her upper lip . . . a twisted little smile that she could stand up to him and make him lose his temper. That at least she could do in retaliation for what he had done in marrying her against her will. There had been no need for that! Knowing her to be imprisoned he could have marched straight off to the American Consulate and kicked up a fuss on her behalf. The Consul would have seen to it that she wasn't treated as Cortez had said roughly that she would have been, without his intervention.

Damn him!

She swung round against the tree and pummelled at the scaly trunk until her hand began to hurt. She leaned there and felt the hot tears come into her eyes. He just wanted her and didn't care a jot that her mind's mosaic of incidents and happenings, of small joys and sudden disasters, had been shattered into fragments that only time and patience would restore to a pattern she would once again recognise and understand.

He was utterly insensitive, and she only wished that she could go to his aunt and ask her assistance in getting away from him. But the woman was as ingrained with Spanish attitudes as her nephew and she would regard it as *escandaloso* if his newly married wife should wish to leave him. She would be as scornful of Arabel's request as of a child asking for plain bread when jam was offered. Her famous nephew was a wealthy man with land, property and livestock of his own; a man to whom other women had thrown their carnations, and she would be stonily deaf to Arabel's plea. 'Grow up,' she would probably say. 'Try to behave like a woman instead of a fool!'

There was Luz, of course, and Juan, to whom she might appeal, but they were under the sway of their elders and would be too afraid of their uncle to risk his displeasure.

Heaven help her, but she was trapped!

She gazed wildly around her and saw only the white stone walls of the *estancia*, the place that had to be her home until she found some way to escape from it.

Bracing her slim shoulders, she made her way back to the patio where *merienda* had been served. Now it was empty. The table had been cleared and the members of the family had gone their various ways ... all that was left were a few tiny bright birds pecking at the crumbs and the sugar left from the cakes.

'That's all I have,' Arabel thought listlessly. 'Everyone thinks I have jam on it, but I know—I know that somewhere, at some time, I met a man and I loved him madly. Now for all I know he might be dead! But if he isn't dead and we meet again, I shall no longer be a free woman but one who is tied to a hateful husband!'

She walked into the house with blazing eyes, throwing glances of sheer disdain at everything in her path, the carved richness of the dark wood furniture against the oriental tiling, the scrolled lamps like something out of a *seraglio*, and the jaguar-skin rugs from a south American jungle.

No doubt he had been to all the Latin countries, that husband of hers, and thrilled the crowds with his cool daring, and collected with his matador gold these treasures for his house. Tall chairs with low-slung arms, the sort used in convents when the nuns had worn flowing habits. Filigreed gates leading from one room to another, gold-framed mirrors, one of which had a painted lady in the centre, screens of leather in a vivid blue, and book cabinets agleam with tulipwood and tortoiseshell.

Don Cortez had certainly made up for a deprived boyhood ... he had invented a grand name for himself and with her assistance he meant to found his own dynasty under the emblem of a bull's head speared upon a sword.

Never! She'd fight him tooth and claw! And as if the devil himself were at her heels Arabel fled upstairs and along the gallery, flinging herself into the apartment where she at least had a room to herself ... for the time being.

She glanced around her and for the first time in this Spanish house felt something akin to pleasure in the pale gold sheen of the floor, partly covered in gaily coloured wool rugs. There was a divan patterned with brilliant bird-of-paradise flowers, a coolly purring fan in the latticed cedarwood ceiling, and wrought-iron flower bowls spilling with flowers. On a little oriental table stood a Spanish casket, and there was a fragrance of lemon verbena from several hanging pomander balls.

A charming sitting-room, made extra special by the deep balcony beyond a pair of lacy iron doors. It was filled with hanging plants and fan-back chairs, and it seemed to hang sheer above the stone courtyards below.

The sun was fading away, Arabel noticed, and a diaphanous veil of flame seemed to float in the sky. The atmosphere still had a warm vibrancy to it, but the shadows of the trees were deeper against the walls that were softly touched with flame. Something rustled in the cascading wistaria, and there was a sudden scent of eucalyptus as a bird disappeared among the coin-shaped leaves that seemed to give off the faintest jingle.

Arabel's hands gripped the iron parapet, and the iron was too solid and the waning sun too flamy for her to believe that she dreamed all this. It was real enough and she could no longer cling to the hope that she was suddenly going to wake up in a prosaic bed somewhere, a mere secretary with no sapphire ring upon her hand.

The red-gold rays of the sun were caught in the stone, but its glimmering beauty filled her with dread rather than admiration. It was a symbol of ownership, not love. Cortez owned her as he did all this, and what he called love would always be three-parts pride in having used nerve and gall to achieve what he had. That was what put the hint of a swagger in his walk, and the gleam of the devil in his eye. He hadn't been born into the lap of luxury, but now he had it and he meant to make the most of it ... and she was included in that feast of the tiger!

The sun went down and fireflies shone their tiny green lights in the dusk. The scents of the gardens grew richer and more heady, and Arabel gave a sudden shiver.

This was to be her wedding night and she was expected to dress in the finery he had bought her and act the starry-eyed bride in front of his family.

She couldn't do it!

A fingernail snapped as her grip tightened upon the wrought iron. But she knew she had to; that he would make her behave with all the proper decorum of a Spaniard's wife. He would dress her himself if she refused to play her part in the ritual, stripping her of this trouser-suit which he didn't care for, touching her with those hands that the cape and the sword had made so adept.

Damn his eyes! Her legs quivered as she turned away from the parapet ... and then she cried out, for a tall lean figure was standing in the entrance to the sitting-room, silent and still as a figure of stone.

'Oh ... it's you!'

Arabel had flung a hand against her mouth ... it was like sorcery, as if her thoughts had conjured him out of the very air. 'You must have the tread of a cat,' she accused. 'I didn't hear you——'

'You were miles away,' he said quietly. 'I could have worn hobnails and you wouldn't have heard me. Were you begging the night gods to waft you away from San Devilla?'

'I—I was wondering what I should wear for dinner,' she replied, and the quiver had moved upwards through the whole of her body. 'I daresay you'll want me to really paint the lily in order to impress your aunt and cousins and any others who are curious about your foreign bride.'

'I'm glad, at least, that you weren't thinking of dining in your boy's suit.' He put a lighter to a cheroot and she saw his face above the flame, wearing a satanic smile. 'Here in southern Spain the world has stood still a little and some of the old-fashioned values are still appreciated, and though we don't pretend, we of the Ildefonso, that we are landed gentry, we do enjoy a little gracious living. And also it would be a pity to have so many charming dresses only to let them repose in your wardrobe when your husband has at least one good eye with which to admire them on your slender figure.'

That keen, dark on gold eye flicked Arabel from her ankles to her hair, which was still tangled from their affray in the palm garden. 'It should please you, Arabel, that I find you attractive and wish to bring out in you all the latent woman.'

'For your own ends,' she said bitterly. 'Your dressed-up doll whom you wish to parade in front of your relatives, and who when you click your fingers must bow and scrape and flatter your masculine ego. If you wanted that, Don Cortez, why didn't you marry a woman of your own country?'

'Have I indicated in any way at all that I want—idolatry?' he drawled. 'And you can't seriously suppose that Andalusian women are so docile? They are the prop and mainstay of most families in this region, while many of the men like to act the *caballero* in the cafés and the flamenco cellars. Believe me, *chica*, I have had my share of smoky taverns and the whirling skirts of the gipsy dancers. I want to enjoy my few thousand acres of bull land and my *estancia*—with my wife.'

'And I must learn your ways,' she rejoined, 'and it would very much suit you if I never remembered a single detail of my former life. You are hoping, aren't you, *señor*, that I remain like this, with my past blotted out?'

He gave a very Latin shrug of his shoulders and smoke ebbed from a slightly twisted corner of his mouth. 'What does it matter? Yesterday has gone and tomorrow is always more promising. Look forward, Arabel, not backward, for as we say in the arena a glance over the shoulder can cost a man a toss on the horn of the bull. A very painful experience, believe me!'

'I'm not afraid of what lies behind me,' she said. 'But you are!'

'Am I really?' Again he shrugged and flicked ash to the tiling of the balcony. 'I have Moorish blood in my veins, and a dash of the gipsy, and I don't question the mysteries of life. Much of what is to be will be, but all the same it does no good to place oneself on a rack of regret for some of the things we do as we go through life. We are but human beings, and each of us has some basic imperfection, even you, my outwardly appearing golden girl. The Moors, in fact, hold to the belief that nothing should be so perfect that the eye of evil fall upon it and cause it some harm.'

'The eye of evil,' she echoed, softly, and her blue eyes were fixed upon the triangular black shadow where the Don's gored eye was blind and dark. 'Perhaps that's how I feel, that it has fallen upon me?'

'Thank you.' He bowed sardonically. 'I shall store up these compliments that you pay me, *querida*, and one day there will be a reckoning and you will repay me for each one.'

'More promises, more threats?' She defied him with a toss of her head, knowing even as she did so that he was possessed of a coiled temper that might spring at her at any moment. She was aware of the iron parapet behind her and the sheer drop to the hard stones of the courtyard ... this was the deep heart of Spain where passions ran high, and a man in his position might get away with many things ... a man who had been idolised as an undefeated *espada* whose sword had been put away with blood on its blade.

'I wonder what it is you are asking for?' The words seemed to come from deep in his throat. 'My aunt would advise me to toss you over my knee and apply to your backside the hard side of a hairbrush——'

'Don't you dare!' Arabel took a sharp step backwards as he took a step towards her. 'I—I won't be treated like a child! I have a right to my opinion of you, and it's just too bad if you don't care for a candid character reading!'

'You aren't reading my palm, my dear, but being a little bit of a shrew.' Again he moved and again she retreated. 'An application of the hairbrush might tame you a little, but on the other hand there is a way of dealing with a wayward woman that would be rather more enjoyable for me.'

Arabel caught his meaning at once and as her spine came up hard against the iron parapet she gave a gasp that was partly pain and partly fear. She had told herself that when the moment came when his Latin passions would want their assuagement she would be as cold and unyielding as a statue of stone. But at his tone of voice and the way he looked so menacing in the half-darkness she felt the blood race furiously through her veins and knew instinctively that she would fight him every inch of the way ... and he would enjoy that. He was still an *espada* at heart and none of his fights had ever been won without the added spice of danger; he would want it that way and would hold to the philosophy that with a bull and a woman you came in as close as you dared.

He came close right now, bending her across the iron without even touching her. Her eyes fought with him and her hands were curled into claws that would rend his lean face, if he allowed her to be that quick.

'There's no pleasure in a tame wife,' he said mockingly, 'that's why I wanted you. From a ragamuffin boy, *querida*, life has been a game of chance for me, and I knew, by the good *Dios* I knew, that marrying me was for you a choice between the devil and the dog. No bride ever looked as white-faced and desperate as you, my dear, and as you say it was as if the devil had come for you. Nonetheless we are man and wife, and I will neither live the unnatural life of a monk, nor will I take a mistress to satisfy what you arouse in me.'

'What are you going to do?' She spoke with nervous intensity. 'Rape me? You know that's what it will be—the act of a rapist!'

'Those are harsh words from soft lips,' he said. 'Would you prefer me to enjoy my leisure with another woman? Come, be quite candid, Arabel. I'm not a doddering impotent and I don't intend to act like one, so what is it to be? Shall I leave you alone in the evenings and return at dawn with the scent of another woman clinging to me? Is that what you want?'

'I—I want to be let off the hook and not have to put up with you in any way at all.' She felt a sudden overwhelming self-pity, bringing the tears that gave a radiant shimmer to her eyes. 'If you had any heart at all you'd let me go b-before we make life a misery between us. I—I thought Spaniards had a sense of honour!'

'Indeed they do have, *querida*, and I think that most of my countrymen would agree that I did the honourable thing in taking for a wife a woman who could well have been put on trial for being a foreign rebel-rouser. They would say that I snatched you from a fate worse than death—ah, such big tears, like great pearls melting in wine.' His lips curled half-mockingly as he brushed a tear from her cheek. 'Shall I treat you like a *niña pequeña* and let you weep on my knee? Perhaps that is what you need, eh? To be a little girl with the papa she never had?'

'Go to the devil,' she said shakily. 'I don't want your damned pity, for what it's worth! You're made of iron and won't unbend where I'm concerned.'

'Then take your choice.' His voice was suddenly harsh and his eye was like the point of a dagger, thrusting into her. 'I can be nice to you, or I can be ruthless, but one thing I am not going to be and that is a beggar for my wife's favours. We both know, don't we, that it would no more please you to have me come home from another woman's bedroom than it would pleasure me. A man doesn't buy a cat and then catch the mice himself. It's you—you I want!'

Her hands were quick, but his arms were swift as whips and he had her lashed to his body in the flick of an eye. His strength was so cruel, she thought dizzily, as he lifted her and carried her with ease into the sitting-room and onwards into the master bedroom, where the lamps diffused a soft, intimate glow. With the stride of a jaguar he seemed to take her towards the big bed ... and then past it, to drop her to her feet in front of the cavernous wardrobe, where she caught her breath in shocked surprise.

He laughed at her, reading in her raised eyes what she had dreaded was about to happen.

'Come,' he swung open the wardrobe doors, 'let us choose a suitable dress for the bride of Ildefonso to wear to her wedding supper. There was no time and no place for any supper when we left Venezuela in such haste, and tonight the table downstairs will be set with the best silver and there will be wine from the *estancia* cellars and a *flamenco* troupe to entertain us in the traditional way. That, at least, is something to anticipate, eh?'

As he spoke he quirked an eyebrow and ran his hand along the array of garments inside the deep robe, his fingers pausing here and there to feel a satiny fabric or one that was smoothly velvet.

'Are you going to choose, Arabel, or will you allow me that intimate privilege?'

'Go ahead,' she said, and still her heart was hammering in her side and still she was unbearably conscious of the great lacy bed and what she had anticipated with regard to it. 'You paid for most of the things and you know what you like.'

'*Ay*, that is one thing a man learns as he goes through life, and it is a fortunate man who can actually have what he likes. Ah, now this seems a suitable dress for a bride.' He drew forth a long-skirted gown in glimmering sapphire-blue velvet, very simple in style because the fabric was so deeply coloured and so gorgeous. His touch played over it almost sensuously ... almost as if he were touching her, and she half-turned away with the colour flaming high on her cheekbones.

'As you wish, *señor*.' She made her voice polite and cool, and strove to uphold her promise to herself, that she wouldn't fight him on any issue and bring out his almost tigerish response to a challenge. 'I'll wear whatever dress you prefer.'

'Come, don't you admire the colour of this one?' he demanded. 'Don't you find the material and the style a charming combination? Don't you care how lovely you will look in this gown?'

She gave a careless shrug of her shoulders. 'I'd as soon wear a skirt and blouse, but you're the master, aren't you? Your wish is to be my command.'

'Are you always going to be so perverse?' He flung the blue dress on to the bed, a gesture that seemed to remind her that she had come dangerously close to being flung there herself.

'You married me,' she said. 'You should have taken into account that unhappy women are on the peevish side.'

'That is how you mean to go on, being peevish and unresponsive to everything I try to do for you?' He towered over her, or he seemed to in his dark-browed anger. 'I'd like to shake you to bring you to your senses, Arabel!'

'Please do it,' she rejoined. 'A thorough shaking might unblock this memory of mine and then I'll know exactly why it is that you—you put all my nerves so on edge that I could scream. Being with you is like waiting for something awful to happen! I—I feel as if I'm poised high up on a window ledge and that at any moment something is going to push me off and I'm going to fall with an awful thud. You scare me, don't you know that—or care?'

She was shivering as she stood there, and with a sudden imprecation in Spanish he turned on his heel and made for his own room, the one that adjoined this larger, more luxurious bedroom. He was gone about two or three minutes, while Arabel remained in the grip of a nervous tremor that wouldn't relax its sudden hold on her. The tensions of the day had caught up with her and she didn't resist when Cortez pushed her down on the ottoman at the foot of the bed and poured a tawny liquid into a globular glass.

'Now drink this,' he ordered, placing the glass in the palm of her shaking hand. 'Don't spill it, child ... ah, let me help you! *Dios mio*, you are a creature all tied up with nerves!'

She felt him sit beside her and raise the edge of the glass to her lips. The liquid was strong brandy and it seemed to burn in her throat as he forced her to drink every drop. He frowned at her, waiting while the cognac took effect on her nervous system and stilled the tremors that shook her.

'You are your own worst enemy, not I,' he said, glowering into the empty glass. 'What do you take me for? Do you think I like it that I put the fear of the devil into you, and all because the horn of a bull tore open my face and cost me an eye? Are you such a milk and water creature that you can't look at me without coming over faint?'

'It—it isn't just your eye,' she gasped. 'It's more than that. It's as if you're wearing a mask all over your face and—and one day I'm going to see behind that mask and everything I've forgotten will come back with a rush—and it will be too late for me to—you'll have had everything your way. I shan't be Arabel Marsha Lennox any more, with a life of my own to go back to. Y-you will have taken everything away from me!'

'Like a thief?' The words came cuttingly from the edge of his lips. 'Not like a lover, but as someone who steals upon you in the dark and takes with violence! *Muy bruto*, that is Cortez, eh? That is why you shiver and shake, because this man who has killed bulls has taken a fancy to you, and every time he touches you, you imagine there is blood on his hands. Bah, you try my patience!'

He surged to his feet and his fingers clenched so hard on the stem of the brandy glass that it suddenly snapped and the bowl fell to the floor and splintered.

Cortez stared down at the shards. 'Stay there,' he snarled, and he went down on his haunches and began to collect up the broken pieces of glass. Arabel stared down at his black head, the lamplight casting a sheen over his hair. He suddenly swore and a bright thread of red ran across the brown skin of his hand.

'Now there is blood on me!' He sucked at his thumb and his eye drilled its irony into Arabel. 'No man calling himself a man should be under the sway of his own passions, least of all a matador, who would very soon be carried from the arena with a hole in him if he wasn't in control of every inclination and every movement of his body. As with a bull, so with a woman!'

'Didn't they carry you from the arena?' she asked, and her voice was strangely faint. 'When you—when you lost your eye?'

'It was my last fight, the last time for me *el*

momento de la verdad, and I walked *avasallando*, and my face did wear a mask, *chica*, a scarlet one.'

'Horrible!' She spread her fingers over her own face. *Avasallando*, like a king, the cheers of the crowd ringing in his ears, for the last time. She almost seemed to see him, the great purple and gold cloak swinging around his lean figure, a tortured smile on his mouth as he accepted the approbation of those who saw only the heroics and not the pain of the fearful injury. Arabel spread her fingers over her own eyes, as if to shut from her mind the image that was so strangely vivid.

'Only a cruel people could enjoy such a spectacle,' she said. 'Like the pagan Romans, cheering as the gladiators butchered each other. Are all Latins so—so greedy for ritual and the sight of someone's agony? Is that why you need me, *señor*—to watch me writhe like a moth on a pin?'

'Little fool——'

'I'm not!' She flung back her hair from her eyes and looked directly into his face, with its look of affinity with the dark forces of Latin life. His single eye was a poniard stabbing into her, holding her moth-like, with the lamplight picking out the golden glints in her hair as she moved it back and forth. 'I'd only be a fool if I thought for one moment that your way of life has left an ounce of compassion in you, a thread of sensitivity, a dash of contriteness for any of those ears that have been hacked off the bulls you have killed. You're an arrogant man, and that's why you were able to stand and bow to the crowd even as the blood poured down your face and you could barely see the people who cheered and crowed because you could take it like that. That must have been quite a moment of triumph for you, Don Cortez. The high spot of your life, walking from that arena with a dead bull on the sand behind you ... and a torn-out eye!'

'The way you speak, *mi vida*, one would suppose you had been there.' He pinned her with his gaze and wouldn't let her go, and the blood still ran from the cut on his hand, falling down to stain the skin rug where he stood. 'Would it please you better if I had cowered there on the sand and wept for a woman to comfort me?'

'I—I daresay there were plenty of women to console you after you were taken to the infirmary to be sewn up. They didn't do a very good job, *señor espada*. They ruined your beauty!'

His lips curled into a totally ironic smile. 'It was never my charming face that the ladies went for, *querida*.'

'Oh, was it your virility and your sheer gall in and out of the arena?'

'Ah, so you have noticed that I am not exactly a *maricón*?' he mocked.

'Even the most idiotic innocent would never take you for a—for one of those.' The colour grew hot in her cheeks as she remembered the feel of him against her, hard, taut, filled to the brim with masculine purpose. 'It's some kind of vanity, surely, for matadors to flaunt the rough scars they receive from all that swift sewing-up in the bullring infirmary? You carry them like medals on your bodies!'

'Everyone is vain about something, *chica*.' His eyes dwelt on her glimmering hair. 'Are you not vain about your golden hair? Other women have to strive for that kind of fairness by way of the dye bottle, and nature gave it to you with an abundant smile. Don't tell me it doesn't please you when you stand in front of a mirror and brush that banner of gold so that it covers your shoulders and the tips of your breasts?'

Arabel tautened where she sat and the room seemed to grow intensely silent as he just stood there looking at her, making her aware of her body, as he was aware of it. Nothing he had yet said to her had been so erotic as those words a moment ago, his voice caressing them . . . almost as if he caressed her.

Slowly he raised a hand to the blinded side of his face and blood ran down on to his shirt cuff. 'The fear of the bull's horn to the *espada* is not unlike the fear of a bride when her lover comes to her. Do you know the meaning of the word *espada*?'

'Sword,' she said faintly. A strange weight seemed to settle on her eyelids as she regarded him, standing there as lean and supple as a sword-blade himself, strong legs closely encased in dark linen, the *guaya-vera* open against the bronze chest.

'That—that cut on your hand should be s-seen to,' she rose quickly to her feet and before he could move she had reached the velvet bellpull and given it a tug. 'I'll get the maid to bring some iodine and adhesive, *señor*. You don't want an infection to set in——'

He began to laugh even before she ceased to speak, putting back his black head and letting forth a mock-ing bellow, as of a matador in a tavern. 'You hell of a little coward, Arabel! *Dios mio*, I might have got you from a convent instead of a prison cell!'

Her eyes flashed blue sparks at him and her nos-trils tensed with temper. 'Oh, you—you give no sym-pathy and want none! You're hardly worth bothering with, but you could stop bleeding all over that rug. Those stains might not wash out.'

'Like sore memories, *chica*? Like hidden thoughts so raw they scuttle away and hide, until they are mended?'

She disdained to answer him and marched into the bathroom, splendidly tiled with *azulejos*, those gorgeous Latin tiles that never seemed to fade, with a circular bath tub sunken into the floor, and taps in the shape of crystal seahorses. Arabel went to one of the mottled marble wash-basins and wet a sponge beneath one of the seahorses; she returned to the bedroom where she knelt down and scrubbed at the bloodstains. Her husband's feet were only inches from her head and his long legs seemed to straddle her . . . like a conqueror.

'Quite the little houseproud woman,' he drawled, 'but I do employ housemaids, and I didn't bring you here to scrub the floors.'

'I'm well aware of why you——' Arabel bit back the words, adding hastily: 'Nice things are easily spoiled, *señor*. You ought to live in a house with sand on the floor, then you'd really feel at home!'

'Telling me that I'm no gentleman?'

'If you like.'

'You aren't exactly a law-abiding little lady, are you?'

'I—I suppose not,' she admitted.

There was the discreet sound of a cough and one of the maids came into the room. 'You rang, *señor*?'

'The *señora* did so, Esperanza. I am cut by glass and she wishes to have me disinfected and taped.'

'Oh—there are remedies in the bathroom cabinet, *señor*. Shall I fetch them?'

'No, we won't detain you.' He quirked an eyebrow at Arabel, who had risen to her feet in some confusion. 'No doubt you are all busy in the kitchen with preparations for our celebration supper?'

'*Si, señor.*' Esperanza glanced from his bleeding hand to the broken glass on the floor. 'Shall I see to that?'

'Yes, but be careful you don't cut yourself as I did. The *señora* is concerned for the rugs.'

'Si, señor.' His irony was lost on the young maid, who opened a cupboard in a far corner of the room and took from it a brush and dustpan. Very soon the pieces of glass were swept up and with a polite face and a bob of her uniformed figure she vanished from the room ... no doubt to carry down to the kitchen a little spicy gossip to add to the shards of the brandy bowl. *Already they are fighting*, Arabel could imagine the girl announcing with glee. *How could it be otherwise?* someone else would add, and there would be knowing nods over the baking meat and the boiling potatoes. *What good to a man like him, a girl like her?*

'You were the one who pulled the bell,' the Don said drily, as he followed her into the bathroom. 'Now the servants are bound to talk and speculate on how well matched we are.'

Arabel tilted her nose and pretended she was scornful of the gossip. Inside the wall cabinet with its triple mirrored doors she found a bottle of TCP, a roll of antiseptic plaster and a small pair of scissors.

'Please hold out your hand,' she requested. He did so, and all the time she attended to him he stood there with a mordant smile on his mouth.

'How very neat,' he said, eyeing the result of her work. 'You should have been around when they went to work on my face.'

'Let's stop talking about *that*,' she shuddered, and turned away from him to replace the medications in the cabinet. He was watching her through the mirrors ... a swift look showed her that the smile had abruptly left his face and there was something oddly searching about the way he was studying her reflection.

'We had better get ready for supper,' she said. 'May I have the bathroom first?'

'You may have it entirely to yourself, *querida.*' He swung away from her and sauntered to the doorway. 'I shall go and use the sauna which is attached to my dressing-room. Some steam and a little meditation might do wonders for my devious soul. *Adios* for now.'

CHAPTER EIGHT

ARABEL'S heart was thudding as she came down the long curve of stairs to the hall, a square of filmy blue silk clenched in her fingers, and a wobbly feeling in her legs.

She wore the glimmering sapphire velvet, with a jewelled cross shining against the simplicity of the dress. The cross had lain on the dressing-table and she had dropped the chain over her head and let the jewelled weight of the lovely thing rest against her bosom because for one day there had been enough friction, and his family would be looking forward to celebrating his marriage... even if in their hearts they doubted if a fiery Latin could be happy with a cool-looking Nordic woman.

Reaching the foot of the staircase, she paused there, gathering breath and nerve for the moment when she must enter the *sala* where the Don's family and friends would be waiting for her. He could have spared her this, she thought fretfully. He could have let her adjust to the *estancia* itself before throwing her to the lions!

Then she stiffened as if electricity had shot through her, a lonely and nerve-racked figure in this hall of arcades and hanging lamps, like something out of a

Moorish legend. Someone had appeared from one of the stuccoed archways, to stand just within the fretted light of one of the lamps. Eyes the clouded gold-brown of amber dwelt upon Arabel, and there was something both sensuous and cruel about the mouth that lay deep red against the golden pallor of the woman's skin. She had deeply slanting cheekbones, and a flower was fastened to the intricate knot of black hair worn at one side of her long neck. Her dress was of black guipure lace, and as she moved further into the lamplight Arabel saw on her feet a pair of high-heeled shoes, as red as her mouth.

The woman might have stepped from the frame of a Velasquez painting; she was lost in time and totally at one with the surroundings of this house.

For moments on end she was only half real to Arabel, and then all at once she spoke and the illusion was lost. The tone of her voice matched the cruel sensuality of her mouth. 'So Ildefonso has lost his head over a piece of golden fluff, whose great Miss Muffet eyes look at me as if I were the black spider come to sit beside her.'

Antagonism flared like a live coal in Arabel and she knew without asking that she was confronted by a woman who had wanted Cortez and had lost out to a foreigner; someone who was much younger than herself, and still possessed of a certain innocence.

The amber eyes flicked Arabel from head to toe, and came to rest on the jewelled cross that shone against her dress. Her eyes narrowed, as if she were speculating on the cost of the gem and for what it had been rewarded.

Arabel drew herself up pridefully, for whatever the secret situation between her and Cortez she had no intention of revealing her inner turmoil and uncertainty to a woman who could be an old flame of his.

Let her think the obvious, that the costly jewel was the gift of a husband whose ardent expectations had not been in vain. That was what he wanted everyone to think, and there was still a remote hope that he might let things remain in a state of siege between them; teetering on the edge of capture rather than being forced to a desperate fight and a bitter victory.

Her fingers crept to the cross and clung there, and she could feel in the atmosphere of this part of the hall a current of tension so acute that she was no longer in any doubt that the Spanish woman was savagely jealous of her; a tigress from whom the choice bone had been snatched, prowling there in the half-shadows, thin and graceful in a feline way.

'I am Riva Montelegre,' the woman said. 'My husband and Cortez were rival matadors and I have been a friend of this family for a long time. None of us expected that Cortez would ever go for a milk-and-biscuit blonde, and you had better be warned that your welcome into our circle is not exactly a warm one.'

'There is no need for a friend of the family to issue warnings to me, Señora Montelegre.' Even as Arabel spoke so coolly she was telling herself, hotly, that she hated Cortez for dragging her into this household where she was like a burr on the back of a mule, one with viciously kicking hooves. His family disliked her because she was alien to them, but this woman had a different reason for pouncing on her in the shadows, like a spiteful cat with red-tipped claws at the ready.

'And tell me, *señora*, is your husband aware of how much to heart you take the marriage of Cortez Ildefonso?'

The woman caught her breath audibly, and Arabel tensed as if half-expectant of feeling those long fingernails at her throat.

'Don't you know—hasn't Cortez mentioned that his best friend and rival was killed in the ring a year ago? Has he not got around to sharing *everything* with you?'

'I'm sorry to hear that your husband is dead.' Now Arabel understood why the woman wore black lace; the period of mourning in Latin countries was a prolonged one, sometimes a lifetime one for some women who cared greatly for the man they had lost. But also Riva Montelegre would be aware that black looked seductive against her matt gold skin, and the jealousy that burned in her had not been ignited at a recent fire. She had hungered for Cortez a long time and the death of her husband would have opened wide the gates of hope that she could plunge into his rival's arms and be consumed in a mutual blaze.

It hadn't happened. In Venezuela he had seen someone younger, whose gold hair had enticed him like a bull to the cape.

'We had better go into the *sala*.' Arabel took that final step to the hall, but when she would have passed Riva Montelegre a sharp-tipped hand reached out and closed on her arm.

'You can't hold him,' Riva hissed, her musky perfume and her hatred like a stormcloud around Arabel. 'You haven't the *sal*, the know-how or any of the Latin woman's capacity for passion. He isn't a cold man, but there's something frosty about you, Miss Muffet.'

'Don't call me that!' Arabel tried to shake off Riva's hand, but the long fingernails dug into her and had she tried to tear free there would have been long scratches on her arm. 'And please let go of me before I raise my voice and call my husband.'

'Oh, but you are too much the little lady to yell out for a man like a fishwife, you with your demure blue eyes and your cloistered air. Half of you is sleep-walking! You are lost in girlish dreams and have about as much idea of a Spaniard's true nature as you have of a tiger's. Your sort are all alike. You run after our men and then find you can't wipe your feet all over them; they have too much dignity for that, and devil enough to look elsewhere when they become bored with a plastic doll masquerading as a woman.'

'If you're such a real woman, why didn't you manage to make him marry you?' Arabel fought back. 'How come he resisted your Latin charms and chose mine instead?'

'Because he felt burdened by guilt, that is why! Because he knew himself in some way responsible for Rogelo's death, getting the crowd worked up like that at Talavera, with his bravado over the loss of his eye. They were always such rivals, and Rogelo wanted to show everyone that he was as daring and tough as Cortez, and he wanted to take up the *capote* that Cortez flung down after Talavera and did not resume again, and so the next time Rogelo fought he chose a Muira bull such as the one which had injured Cortez. I knew that my husband would be no match for that terrible creature, and so did Cortez, but he made no attempt to dissuade Rogelo from fighting the bull ... knowing as I did that if the Muira killed my husband then he and I could be together openly without any scandal to upset his relations. He had influence over Rogelo, as over most people, but after the fatal goring of my husband he went abroad as if he had a sudden attack of conscience, and I was left in despair, not knowing what to think. It was selfish of him, sudden and ruthless, but that is his way. He stayed away travelling, and then finally he returned to Andalusia ... married to you!'

Riva's spate of words swept over Arabel like a rip-tide taking hold of her, and she stared into the Spanish eyes as if mesmerised ... eyes with curving lashes like miniature lace fans.

'You—you are a sop to his conscience,' Riva cried contemptuously. 'Part of a mood which will swiftly pass when he realises that you have only immature emotions to offer in exchange for his, which are fully adult and honed on a hard, fighting life. Tell me, what does the bullfight mean to you? Do you understand any of its significance? Of course not! It is written all over your naïve face what you think of the *corrida*. Little fool, one would suppose you were unaware that you married one of Spain's foremost *espadas*—or didn't it matter so long as you knew he had made lots of money from it?'

'Don't you accuse me of marrying Cortez for his money!' Arabel wrenched free of Riva's fingers, flinching as the nails tore her skin. 'I couldn't have cared less how rich he was, or how poor. It never entered my head ... I—I had only one reason for marrying him!'

Arabel fell abruptly silent, watching as the red lips of Riva curled in scorn. 'Love?' she exclaimed. 'What would you know about loving a matador? They aren't like other men; they are like the tamers of tigers, or those who climb high mountains to conquer them. Have you ever seen Cortez at work, have you?'

'I—no.' Arabel shook her head. 'We met after he—he had retired from the bullring.'

'Then how can you say you love him, for that is what you meant, eh, when you say you had only one reason for marrying him? He fascinates you, as he would a little milksop not long out of the classroom! You like the idea of the danger inherent in him, but had you ever seen him in action you would have covered your blue eyes and shivered with all the puritan horror of the novice.'

Riva's eyes burned darkly and she looked the very embodiment of the Latin *femme fatale*; her hair gleamed like black satin and there was the sensuality to her of tropic flowers and spice gardens. She must have struck an answering chord in Cortez; that torch she carried must have seared him ... was it true, Arabel wondered, that a sense of guilt had kept him from claiming the widow of his best friend? He was every inch a Spaniard and they carried honour to extremes, and he might have considered her widowhood made her sacrosanct and that by stamping out their mutual flame of attraction he made some kind of retribution to his dead rival.

But flames didn't go out that easily and Arabel could see them smouldering in Riva's eyes, and she knew herself hated as only a woman could hate who had been thrust out of her lover's arms and had to accept that he had taken another woman into them.

'I knew Cortez before he retired from the bullring ... before he acquired this sudden taste for the insipid wine of the Americans. They flung roses at his feet when he walked through the streets of Seville, Madrid, any place in Spain or South America or Mexico. To the *aficionados* he was a great artist who could bring the crowd to its toes whenever he unfurled his great cape and made one of his close and daring *veronicas*, and when he killed with his black head uncovered and the sword like a flick of lightning in his hand. See, you shudder at the image of it!'

Riva gave a contemptuous laugh. 'What can you give him that he won't very soon find tedious and boring? You are like rice and syrup in the teeth of a man who prefers chilli peppers and *manzanilla*. You caught him on the rebound, when with all the fine flourish of the *espada* he decided that he couldn't dishonour the memory of Rogelo by marrying his widow. He decided to put a barrier between us, but look what he chose! A flimsy young girl in a blue dress, wearing his crucifix with all the frigid piety of a little nun! You won't remain much of a barrier for long, *azul* eyes. I mean to sweep you right out of my way!'

As she said this Riva turned with sudden quick and feline grace towards the lean, masculine figure who was suddenly crossing the hall towards them.

'Ah, Juan, you have been sent to fetch us to the party, eh?' Riva gave a laugh that was melting with charm. 'How handsome you look, *niño*. Watch out or you will have your cousin's girl bride falling in love with you!'

Still laughing, she moved away in the direction of the brightly lit *sala*, from out of which came the sound of vivacious Spanish voices, all talking at once it seemed, relatives, friends and neighbours, greeting the *padrón* on his return from far places ... unexpectedly married to a foreigner.

'Cortez sent me to bring you——'

'I can't, Juan!' She clung to his arm in sudden terror, unnerved by her confrontation with Riva Montelegre, and the sound of all those people waiting to look her over ... like some *palomina* filly the *padrón* had got himself on his travels.

'Perdoname?' Juan gazed down at her pale face, boyishly perplexed by the look of obvious fear in her eyes.

'I—I can't face it, Juan! Please make my excuses—say I'm not feeling well. Cortez will understand—surely?'

'Cortez will be furious, is what you mean,' his cousin replied, casting a glance towards the *sala* and frowning. 'What did she say to you, the Montelegre woman? Was she unkind, and is that why you shrink from the party?'

That scene with Riva had been incredible, outrageous, charged with the emotions of two women who felt justified in blaming one man for their unhappiness. Arabel would have given her soul not to see Don Cortez ever again, but how was she going to avoid seeing him within the next few minutes when even a nice boy like Juan wouldn't conspire to help her escape that moment when she must walk into that room of Latins and have Cortez claim her in front of them all?

'Come, you are *muy linda* and have nothing to fear from anyone,' Juan urged, looking her over and letting the admiration show in his dark eyes.

'You just said, Juan, that my husband would be furious with me if I ran out on his party like a rabbit.' She tried to smile, but it was an effort.

'You are not a little *cobarde*, are you?'

'A coward? I wonder—Riva Montelegre implied certain things about your cousin—my husband.' Arabel met Juan's eyes and searched them. 'Do you know if they were ever—lovers?'

Juan fidgeted and looked rather embarrassed. 'It would be in the past, if it was ever so. Matadors—you know how it is, the danger makes them fascinating to all sorts of women.'

'Even married women,' she said. 'She told me that her husband was killed in a bullfight which Cortez might have prevented . . . I had the feeling she implied that he didn't attempt to dissuade Rogelo in the hope that he would be—killed, and that afterwards he had an attack of conscience and—and ran out on her by—by marrying me. Juan, could that possibly be true?

Could he do a thing like that? He is rather—no, he is ruthless, isn't he?'

'I—suppose so.' Juan lifted his shoulders in a shrug. 'A man in his profession, Arabel, what can you expect? He learns rules and tricks that he applies to everyday life, but it is all in the past. You are the one he married and you must be aware that the alliance of man and woman in our part of Spain is as unbreakable as a ring of iron. Whatever Riva Montelegre meant to him, and we knew, we of his family, that there was talk of a certain woman at Talavera who had importance in the eyes of Cortez, it never came to anything, did it? He went abroad, he found you, and now he wishes to show you off to his friends.'

'Like an ornament he has added to his collection of swords, capes and medals?' she asked, a note of cynical despair in her voice. 'I'm shaking in my shoes, Juan. I'm begging you to help me.'

'But I see no reason for it, Arabel. You look pale, but you aren't on the point of collapse—are you?' A whimsical note came into his voice, which seemed to deepen and make a man of him. 'You are pretty as the flowers on the golden bell tree in the *corte*. You will be much admired, and don't all women like to be looked upon with pleasure?'

'Is that their sole function in the eyes of southern Spaniards?' she asked. 'Are you also imbued with the Moorish idea that women were made to please, and to be dominated?'

'Is it such a shock to you, little *yanqui*?' His eyes laughed down into hers, and for a fleeting moment she almost seemed to realise what Cortez had looked like when he was bordering on manhood, less muscular, less arrogant, less of all the things he had become over the years. Even Juan couldn't realise just how dominating a man like Cortez might be, with a woman in his arms. He would want totality, her complete submission and response, and he would use every ounce of his ruthless skill to make a slave of her.

To Juan he was an older cousin, a lord of the land, self-made but nonetheless important. Whatever he did would be perfectly all right in the eyes of his relations, who looked upon him not only as a hero but as a generous provider who gave them a good home.

It was no use, Arabel thought. She might as well face up to the fact that she was the property of Cortez and should think herself not only grateful but highly honoured. She tilted her chin and fingered the jewelled cross, as if it might give her the courage she so badly needed. 'Very well,' she said, 'let us go and face the lions.'

Don Cortez was standing at the centre of the group of people gathered together in the lovely, long *sala*, under the light of the wrought gold chandeliers. He was turned in profile to her so she couldn't see the triangular black patch on the left side of his face; she saw only the firmly chiselled line of that right profile, the thrusting power in brow, nose and chin. His black hair was well groomed and beneath his dark dinner jacket he wore a waistcoat of brocade, a shirt of creamy linen and tapering trousers.

As he raised a wine-glass to his lips the wide gold band gleamed on his hand, and Arabel felt her heart turn over.

This was how the doomed queens of Henry VIII must have walked to the block, she thought, as she made her way down the length of the room, almost silently in her velvet dress. Eyes began to turn towards her, but he waited with the stillness he must have practised in the arena when he knew the bull was drawing close to him, waiting with diabolic nerve and patience for the moment when he swung to face the horns, the *capote* flaring out to bedazzle his opponent.

Darn you . . . darn you, Arabel cried silently, *you're making me come to you in front of all these people. Then what will you do, make me kiss you?*

He swung precisely to face her the very moment she reached his side, and she saw at once the challenging tilt to his black eyebrows and the faint quirk of mockery on his mouth. The training and instinct of the matador made him swift to pick up vibrations and he knew what was going through Arabel's mind as he leaned over her, as if poised for that wifely kiss in front of his family and his guests. Then, sensing that she was about to back away from him, he caught her by the hand and carried that to his lips, burying them against her wrist where her pulse beat a maddened tattoo.

'We were beginning to think that you had decided not to join us, *mi esposa,*' he drawled. 'As I was explaining to everyone, Arabel, you are on the shy side and it takes time for you to adjust to new faces and new surroundings. Well, my friends,' he drew her to his side and she felt his hand pressing against her waist, 'this is the girl I could not resist bringing home to San Devilla. Can you blame me?'

There was laughter and several people drew nearer to her, expressing their delight in meeting her, yet with reservations in their eyes that Arabel couldn't help but notice. Someone handed her a glass of wine, and there by a screen of glowing leather was a figure in black lace; a fan of the same lace held like a half-mask against her face in order to intensify those pin-points of hatred in her eyes as she watched Arabel, a blue and gold figure against the dark distinction of the man whom Riva regarded as hers.

'Drink your wine and then we go in to dinner.' The lean hard fingers pressed deep in the velvet covering Arabel's slim shape, and she shot up at him the briefest of looks, curious to see if he had noticed Riva. Her fingers clenched the stem of her glass, for he was gazing directly across the room at the other woman and his face had a carved stillness about it, as if he rigidly suppressed whatever he was feeling or thinking as he read what lay in Riva's eyes.

'Drink!' he said again, and Arabel obeyed him even as she felt a strong inclination to fling every drop of the wine into the face of his mistress. So intense was the urge that she gulped the wine before she plastered that satiny hair to the sloping cheekbones and spoiled the guipure lace that covered the catlike figure.

Fingers locked themselves about her elbow and she was led into the dining *sala*, where a long oval table was laid gleamingly with silver and crystal, and there was a scent of carnations and smilax. She was placed at her husband's right hand, while his aunt was seated at his left side. As Arabel unfurled her napkin she wondered about this ... did it remotely worry him that she found his scarred and blinded eye hard to take?

A superb meal was served. Quail the size of partridge, white-fleshed and tasty. Oyster crabs and huge shrimps with a delicious sauce. *Filets* of tender meat, garnished with egg, rice, onions, tomatoes and peppers. Nectarines in cream, and finally a tall cake covered in icing and hung with tiny bells, each one of real gold which each guest kept as a keepsake of the Don's wedding supper.

All through that long meal Arabel was conscious of Riva at the other end of the table, making conversation with those at either side of her, and to all appearances a sophisticated woman of the world. But under that poised exterior there was a tigress who had been thwarted and not for one moment did Arabel relax; the tension had tied knots in her stomach and she picked at the food, and when it came to eating a portion of her own wedding cake she felt suddenly nauseated and went ice-white about her lips and nostrils. Don Cortez cast a keen look at her, seeing as usual more with his single eye than many people saw with two eyes. He rose abruptly to his feet.

'My friends, I think we might all go out to the patio and enjoy the *flamenco*,' he said. 'The night is a mild one, so I am sure you ladies will be sufficiently warm in your silks. Come, we have a very fine troupe to entertain us.'

Chairs were pushed away from the table and there was a general movement towards the archway that led out to the patio, where the guitars could already be heard. Arabel didn't glance at her husband, but she was grateful that he had brought the supper to an end; out there amidst the lanterns and the glimmer of stars she would not be so conspicuous: so much the centre of attention. She might even manage to slip away and leave these Latins absorbed in the strange singing, like echoes from across the Moroccan desert, wailing above the rhythmic beating of the man's heels on the stones of the patio.

Above the scene the fronds of the palms whispered and the scents of the roses and wallflowers mingled to make a heady incense that made it utterly believable that long ago Andalusia had been chosen by the Moors for their harems and palm gardens to flourish in. The warm and sensuous atmosphere of the land might almost have been an extension of their own Orient, and out of all that had grown the beautiful dark faces of the people, and the music that throbbed with a deep, haunting passion.

When there came a lull in the entertainment, the house servants went round pouring wine and *manzanilla*, and the smoke of strong cigars blended with the scents of junipers, oleander and aromatic gum-trees. Huge rose-flowered oleanders and violet Judas trees with tropical lilies clustered beneath them.

Arabel glanced around her, studying the scene, and all at once she gave a shiver, the kind that was referred to as the brushing past of a ghost. She knew the scents of the flowers and there was something more familiar than strange about the throb of the guitars and the click, click of those tiny tortoiseshell castanets on the fingers of the gipsy girl in her scarlet dress.

This wasn't the first time she had stood among the trees and flowers of a Spanish garden and listened in the night to the music that was both fiery and soulful, filled as much with nostalgia as the yearning to be loved.

Who was it she had yearned for? Whose touch had suddenly awakened her to the need to be part of someone else, no longer alone but able to melt skin-close to another human being, there to find the hunger and the giving that gave life a sudden vibrant meaning?

Happiness ... had she found it, only to have it snatched away and replaced by the autocratic possession of the Spaniard who stood just beyond the faintly swaying light of a lantern hung in the branches of a Judas tree?

Don Cortez raised the cigar to his lips and nodded in affirmation of what his fellow Spaniard was saying to him. What were they discussing ... the latest *corrida*, the price of livestock, or the satisfaction gained from being one's own master, with land to pass on to one's very own son?

No ... Arabel was looking around wildly for a means of escape, when into the chiselled frame of one of the Moorish archways stepped a figure in black lace. She was holding something in her right hand, and she spoke into a sudden lull in the festivities. 'Everyone, I have a little ceremony to perform,' her voice and her manner demanded attention, and nearly everyone stopped talking in order to listen to her. 'I have a wedding gift for the young bride, which I am sure you will all consider most appropriate to the occasion. Arabel,' she slowly raised the object which she was holding, 'I hope you will like this. I couldn't think what to buy you as Don Cortez is able to provide all that your heart desires, and then it occurred to me that you would probably be a lover of animals—aren't you all, you foreigners with your quaint ideas?—and so I chose these.'

It was an ornamental cage that she held out to Arabel, and it was filled with the soft twittering of tiny coloured birds. The light of the lanterns had awakened them and they were flying at the curving bars of the cage and beating their delicate wings against them. Arabel stared in frozen amazement at the cage, and the next moment it was forced into her hand and she felt the hard stare of Riva's eyes. 'Are you not going to thank me?' Riva drawled.

Birds in a cage, captive and afraid, longing with all their tiny hearts to be free of the bars that kept them from flying away!

'How dare you!' The words broke in a cry from Arabel's lips. 'You knew I'd hate such a thing—little birds trapped like this. Look, they're beating their wings and hurting themselves!'

Arabel knew only one thing, that the birds had to

be set free, and carrying the cage she forced her way through the throng of wedding guests and suddenly began to run towards the *mirador* that towered above the patio. From up there she would let them go, so they could reach the trees and be safe among the sheltering leaves.

'Arabel!' The name thundered out behind her, but she kept on running, in through the arched entrance of the Moorish tower, her free hand gripping her long skirt as she hastened up the twisting stairway. The birds twittered in their fright, and she felt her heart thudding with hatred of that vindictive woman who somehow sensed that Arabel was like them ... held captive by the iron bars of the *estancia*.

Up and up, with only the starlight through the little windows to show her the way. Behind her came the pursuing feet of Don Cortez, and again his voice rang out, echoing in the well of the spiral stairs. 'Stay where you are, Arabel! Don't venture another step ... the tower balcony is unsafe!'

She heard him but didn't heed him. Above her she could see the milky night sky beyond the arabesqued opening that led out on to the balcony, and within the cage the little birds had grown frantic. She had to set them free, and with a swirl of blue velvet she was out there on that narrow platform, stumbling a little on some broken stone, fumbling blindly with the latch of the bird cage. 'Fly! Fly away,' she urged, as the latch gave and the cage door flew open. But now the birds wouldn't budge, they huddled quivering against the bars, and as she moved forward to the parapet of the balcony she felt the swaying underfoot but was determined to release the birds.

'You crazy little fool!' Hands hooked out of the semi-darkness, but she eluded them and held the cage on the parapet so its tiny captives could feel the beckoning freedom of the night air.

'You do realise that this balcony could break away beneath you at any moment,' Cortez said, and his voice seemed to strike at her like a lash, and she could imagine the furious anger of his face that she should behave like this in front of his friends, making a spectacle of herself instead of acting the demure bride.

'So what?' she said recklessly. 'Your vindictive mistress can take the blame if I fall . . . why in hell did you marry me when she was waiting here to fall into your arms?'

'Arabel, you must see reason. Come now, step carefully back to me and take my hand——'

'So it can rescue me in public and slap me down in private?' she asked, and then to her relief the first little bird hopped out on to the parapet, gave a tiny cheep and flew off towards the trees. Soon the others had followed and one by one they vacated the cage, and when it was at last empty Arabel flung it over the iron rail and watched it fall to the courtyard, where the party guests were clustered in the lantern light, gazing upwards at the *mirador* and her slender figure outlined by the big southern stars.

'There will be no recriminations if you do as you are told and come in off that balcony. Arabel!' His voice grew harsh. 'Do I come out to you and make it certain that the platform gives way and both of us go crashing to the stones below? Make up your mind. In sixty seconds I shall join you——'

'You just can't resist the heroics, can you, *señor*?' Arabel gave a shaky laugh. 'I wouldn't want to be responsible for the fall of a hero, and I will come in —if you make me a promise *and keep it*.'

'What kind of a promise?'

She could just make him out, standing there as

tensed as if he faced a moment of truth in the arena. 'That you will not insist,' she said quietly, 'on being my husband.'

'I have already told you, our marriage is unbreakable in the eyes of my church!'

'You know very well what I mean, *señor.*' She stood there, feeling that menacing vibration beneath her feet at the slightest movement she made. 'I know you won't divorce me, but if you insist that I remain at San Devilla then I must have, at least, the freedom of my—my own bedroom. You must give me that, or come and claim *all* your matrimonial rights out here on this death-trap.'

'You are making terms with a gambler, Arabel. You are throwing down a gauntlet that I may dare to snatch up.'

'Then dare, Don Cortez!' Arabel tossed back her hair and even as she challenged him she felt beneath her the shifting stonework that wouldn't endure their combined weights; if he tried to snatch her off the balcony it would probably collapse and they would hurtle together to the stony pavement of the patio ... and she knew, instinctively she was sure that within the next few seconds he would leap forward, grab her in his arms and defy the gods of chance.

It was no use ... unlike those birds she couldn't fly to the sheltering trees, and neither could she subscribe to yet another legend about Cortez Ildefonso ... that like fateful lovers they had died in each other's arms. She passed her tongue over dry lips and took a step in his direction ... the sway of the balcony had become sickening and she paused and felt her heart beating in her throat.

'Another step, and then another,' he said, and now his voice was low, as if he feared that its vibration might add to the danger of the balcony. She knew he was holding out his hand, for she caught the faint glimmer of his wedding ring; with his other hand he was gripping the side of the doorway as if to brace himself for the moment when he caught her by the hand and pulled her to safety.

'I—I don't think I can move,' she said shakily. 'You're right about me being a fool——'

'I shall wring a certain neck for this! Come, *chica*, two more steps and you have made it. Come!'

'I——' she swallowed and closed her eyes, for it might work if she tried walking the rest of the way blindly.

'For what it is worth, Arabel, you have that promise,' he said. 'Does that assist you in any way? It had better, or we are both done for!'

'Stay there,' she said, 'I'm coming ...'

When it happened, when she felt firm ground underneath her again, she lost her entire grip on everything and didn't feel the Don's arms when they closed around her and carried her down the winding stairs to ground level. Her head lolled unaware against his shoulder, her fleur-de-lys hair tumbling against his dark suiting. His face was grim as he emerged with her from the *mirador*.

'Go home, everyone,' he said harshly. 'The wedding supper is over!'

CHAPTER NINE

Now what? Arabel often asked herself that question in the days that passed and gradually turned into weeks. Whatever the answer to that question, this hiatus had given her a chance to adjust to the *estancia* and to find it an intriguing place ... not that it ever felt like a real home, where she was the real mistress, but more like a halfway house where she was waiting to find her real self.

The quick morning sunlight always amazed her, lancing sheer gold across her bed so that she very soon felt the urge to rise and shower and be out in it. She discovered that she liked the glowing atmosphere that etched everything into pictures ... the great bulls on the plains, the sky like a painted ceiling where carmine, gold and diaphanous green mingled at sun-up, and then when the sun went down in the evening. Then came a scented stillness and the soft flutter of petals down over the tracery of stone and iron in the various courtyards of what she discovered to be a very large estate.

Several times she was driven into the nearest township with the Don's aunt and Luz in attendance. And again the atmosphere was Moorish, with narrow cobbled streets that wended their way into colourful plazas where orange trees hung against white walls and there were central fountains where some of the women still collected their water in head jars. The shops were like dens in the thick walls, tangy and spicy and filled with the kind of foods and goods that aroused the imagination as nothing in a European supermarket ever could.

The Don was generous with pocket money and they were able to buy the oriental-looking sweets, and to sit in the pastry shop and eat Madeira custard cake, or tiny wild strawberries dipped in a syrup of grated nuts topped with whipped cream.

It was like being a schoolgirl again, even though Arabel couldn't remember what her adolescence had really been like. She had been told that she had grown up in an orphanage, but somehow she had the feeling that she had not been unhappy. The emotional trauma had entered her life later on, there in Venezuela, a Latin country that explained why she sometimes breathed a scent, heard a snatch of music, or ate something that for a brief flash was familiar to her.

It was these odd flashes of awareness that made life bearable, for she couldn't have borne it had her mind and senses been totally barren of anything pertaining to her former life. These were the gleams of hope that some day soon she would wake up knowing all about herself . . . and about the man who had married her.

In the meantime she got acquainted with the customs of Andalusia, and with the people whom she found kind, courteous and very superstitious. It was *duende*, Luz informed her, something in Latin people drawn from some deep well of primitive feeling. Like their music, like their passions, they were filled with fire and yet reserved; a sensual people without it being necessary for the girls to show their legs in silly short skirts, or for the young men to lose interest in the courtship of a girl from behind the iron *reja* of her balcony. What can be touched, went the saying, can be had within the hour.

Arabel gave in to the fascination of the deep south, and she gradually found her way about the huge *estancia,* built of thick chunky stone to withstand the hot sun and the winds of the *solano*, and to sustain a certain coolness within its walls, aided by the batwing fans that purred continuously through the day, blending with the cicadas in the courtyards.

She enjoyed making her way to the big kitchen, there to watch the cook patting and slapping the *tortillas*, so much enjoyed by the *vaqueros* who minded the bulls and the sleek, long-maned horses. These enormous pancakes were then baked on a griddle, stuffed with meat, vegetables, or fruit, and rolled like long sausages. They were delicious, and Arabel would sit at the big scrubbed table and tuck into one which had been stuffed with raisins and slices of apricot. She was aware that the staff thought of her as *muy joven*, the Don's *chica* with her golden hair plaited down her spine, but they were tolerant of her because she didn't interfere with their household routines. It was as if a companion for Luz and Juan had come to live in the house rather than a wife for the *padrón*.

They knew, how could they help but know, that he slept *solo* in his austere bedroom, and never visited the canopied *cama* in which Arabel slept.

She felt sure Cortez didn't like it that their impersonal relationship could not be kept a secret from his family or his servants. He was too proud, too much the Latin to enjoy the gossip she had caused him, and more than once she noticed the grim set to his features when they dined, or when he happened to enter a room where she might be having a lively discussion with his cousins, or taking guitar lessons from Hilario Lopez, who had worked with him in the bullring and was now his associate in the breeding of stud bulls.

Arabel knew that a restrained anger burned within Cortez, and she sometimes wondered how long he would abide by his promise to let her live here as his wife in name alone. At night she knew he paced the patios like a man whose tethered patience was wearing very thin, and she would stand very still and quiet on her balcony and listen to the steady tramp of his boots on the stone paving, the cheroot glowing red as he drew on it, the *guyavera* open to his belt, his hair still tangled on his forehead from the late ride he always took over the *sabana*, the wide grasslands where his magnificent bulls must mock him for allowing a slip of a girl to drag from him a promise that went against the very grain of his conquering nature.

He, Cortez Ildefonso, an unbeaten matador of the first rank, held at bay by a pair of stricken blue eyes. Such a thing had never happened to him before! All his life he had taken the bull by the horns; even when ripped and gored he had stood his ground. But up there on that perilous *mirador* Arabel had somehow pierced him where it really hurt ... she had been prepared to fall all those feet to the hard tiling rather than give in to him, and she knew that bitter, injured pride was smouldering in his veins and one of these nights it would erupt and she would be in the direct pathway of all that scalding anger; here in this room with its lamps throwing filigree patterns against the ceiling, and its pomander balls swaying on their silk chains.

She grew to fear the nights, for there were no keys to keep him out of her room. The ruby-shaded light gleamed on the blade of a Toledo sword hung against the panelling of the wall, the hilt chased with black and silver arabesques. She slowly raised herself on one elbow and stared at the sword, the *espada* that represented the man who had often wielded it. Its blade was slim and gleaming and looked very lethal, and she felt as strangely afraid of it as she did of the man to whom it belonged. Suddenly that twinge of fear became a challenge; it was foolish nonsense to be afraid of an inanimate object, as if it could come to life and do her some harm. Only in the hand of Don Cortez was it harmful, and as if drawn to feel it in her own hand, for some strange illogical reason, Arabel slipped out of bed and made her way across the room. She allowed her fingers to trace the black and silver chasing on the hilt, and in and out of her mind moved an image of a menacing, harlequin figure also clad in black and silver. She lifted the sword from its hook and felt its sudden weight dragging at her wrist, and in her imagination that figure in the suit of lights seemed to draw closer ... *think* ... *oh, think*, she was urging herself. There was something here that she was close to remembering, and she gazed at the glimmer of the blade in the lamplight and wanted to tear aside with it the obscuring veil that concealed the reason why she shrank from the man who was her husband.

What had he done to make her feel so disturbed in his presence? Why did she feel this sense of being haunted by some awful happening that he had made her part of? Why had he married her when he knew she had some horrific reason for hating him; binding her to him in a Latin marriage from which there was no easy release? Divorce was out of the question, and even an annulment took years before the separation was granted.

Had he married her to punish her, when he knew only too well that he could have informed the American authorities that she was under arrest in that Venezuelan prison?

She gripped the sword and wished desperately that it would cut her free from the frustration of her lost memory.

'If you aren't careful with that you will cut off a toe or two,' a voice drawled from behind her. 'It's a Toledo blade and sharp as flame ... what are you doing with it, planning to murder me?'

For a second or two Arabel was tense with nerves, and then suddenly her grip relaxed on the sword and it fell out of her hand and slithered on the floor close to her bare feet. He came over and picked it up and his brows were drawn blackly together. 'These things are dangerous if they aren't handled properly. If you had said you were interested I would have shown you how to handle one without clumsiness.' He held the weapon and his lean fingers wandered over the chasing where hers had been. 'Beautiful, is it not?'

'How often have you killed with it?' she asked coldly.

'This particular sword I have never used in the arena,' he replied. 'It was given to me as a present, by someone I greatly revered. This person came across it in an antique shop in Seville and had it polished and made as good as new. I treasure it, and I hope you hadn't some dark design in mind when you took it down off the wall.'

'Like Jael,' she asked, 'who slew the warrior while he slept?'

A smile twitched at the edge of the Don's mouth. 'I believe you would be capable of that,' he said, and flicked a glance over the sheer flowing fabric of her nightdress. 'Shall we put it to the test?'

At once he made her burningly aware of her state of undress and she felt an instinctive urge to dive back into bed ... except that he might take that as an acceptance of his challenge. She glanced around for her robe and saw that it had fallen to the carpet at the side of the bed. She went to retrieve it and was pulling its folds around her when he turned from hanging the sword back on the wall.

'I brought you something—ah, there it is in that box on the silk armchair. I was so distracted by the sight of you, *querida*, studying my sword as if it held some great significance for you, that I quite forgot I had a gift for you. Take off your robe!'

'I shall do nothing of the sort!' Colour flamed in her cheeks and she tightened the sash of her robe. 'Don't think you can buy me!'

'I never supposed at any time that you could be

bought.' With a sardonic air he opened the box and there was a rustle of tissue paper as he withdrew a white fur bedjacket trimmed with ermine tails. 'I saw this in a shop and it so amused me that I couldn't resist buying it. Come, off with that robe—is it a man's, by the way, all camelhair and big lapels?—and let me see how you look in this.'

'I—I prefer my own robe.' It was one of the garments he had not bought her, serviceable, concealing, and a coat of armour that she didn't intend to remove so she'd be vulnerable again in the peach-hued nightdress.

'Why do you have to look like such a woman and behave like such a child?' he asked quizzically, and he started to approach her with the bedjacket held in his hands, his fingers deep in the fur. 'I take the trouble to bring my wife a piece of frivolity that I think she might like and she behaves as if I bring her a snake in a box. Do you think I have an ulterior motive in bringing you a bedjacket? Is that why you look at me with such large and accusing eyes?'

'I—I'm fully aware, *señor*, that you don't like people to know how things are between us, but you made me a promise and if you break it——'

'What then shall I be?' Now he was close to her, his gaze travelling over her gold hair loosened against the drab colour of her robe. 'Will your opinion of me be any worse than it is right now? Whatever I do I am condemned by you, even when I merely wish to see what you look like in this jacket. Don't the fur tails amuse you? Come, relax for once and try to pretend that I am a harmless boy like Juan.'

'Were you ever harmless?' She gave an involuntary laugh. '*Señor*, you emerged into this world like—like that sword emerged from the forge, poised and taut with potential danger. Long ago you might have looked like Juan, but there the resemblance stopped. He is nice, but you—you're an enigma. Really, did you ever suppose when you married me that we could live as a normal couple? Your servants are tolerant of me, but they sense that I have this mental block, and your niece Luz was quick to realise that I knew nothing about you, beyond that I woke in hospital to find myself married to you. Your aunt—she thinks I'm *loca*, and I daresay she has mentioned the fact to you. Damn you, Cortez, for ever bringing me here! It hasn't proved amusing for either of us, has it?'

'It was never meant for that, *querida*. You needed a home and I provided one for you. You needed protection——'

'From you,' she cut in. 'I need to be protected from you, with your insidious gifts—I won't wear that thing, so take it away! Give it to your mistress! I'm sure she'd appreciate the ermine tails!'

'If you are referring to the Señora Montelegre, then let me tell you this,' he leaned suddenly near to Arabel and flung the bedjacket to one side so that he could grip her by the arms. When she tried to wrench free of him he tightened his grip and she could feel him bruising her in his sudden anger. 'Riva was the wife of a friend of mine and I don't go around seducing that kind of woman. I enjoyed her company, as I did Rogelo's, but that is all.'

'That wasn't what she told me, and if I have to believe anyone then I choose to believe her.' Arabel glared up at him, her eyes shimmering in the frame of her hair. 'She said you wanted her husband out of the way so the pair of you could be married—what stopped you, Cortez? Was it the stab of conscience because you did nothing to stop him from fighting that killer bull?'

'Don't talk childish nonsense,' he gave her a shake.

'As if one *espada* ever said to another, don't fight that particular bull, my friend, he might scratch you in the ring, or make a nasty hole in your suit of lights. *Demonio*, what an idea! It was Rogelo's own business if he wanted to fight a furious bull, and I—I had other business which needed my close and personal attention. I am not anyone's keeper, Arabel, other than being yours.'

'My keeper,' she rejoined, 'who paces those courtyards like some tamer who longs to use his whip in order to get his creature to perform for him. You made me a promise——'

'In the name of hell don't go on about that promise!' he gritted his teeth and they made a white bar against the sun-clawed darkness of his skin. 'With you, let me tell you, I have been softer than with any other female I have ever known. Real women like a show of force, a touch of male dominance, but you have it fixed in your brain that I'm your cruel oppressor whose every look, every touch is another form of tyranny bordering on rape. My patience grows very thin, Arabel. It is being stretched to its limit and it might well tear asunder if you again tell me to go to a mistress with the things that I buy for you. Now off with this unattractive garment and on with that fur jacket!'

Impatiently and none too gently he pulled off her robe and flung it to the floor, and it was then that his hands came into contact with her warm body through the peachy silk of her nightdress. She felt his abrupt stillness, his tension, and she saw his flash of temper replaced by something far more frightening, and in that instant Arabel realised what a fool she had been to put up a fight against wearing the ermine-trimmed jacket.

She trembled as his hand ran the length of her

spine and paused at its base where her body curved. The heat of his hand struck through the fine silk and even as she tensed and made ready to spring away from him, his other arm locked itself about her waist and she was imprisoned and pinned against the black silk kimono that he had on. Instantly she knew that it was all he had on and that beneath the black silk his body was hard and bare.

Panic flared and the movements she made in her effort to break free only seemed to intensify the desire that she felt in him. He bore her backwards across the bed and his face above hers was dark, lean and remorselessly in the grip of the passion he had held in check but could no longer restrain. It had hold of him with a pent-up hunger that made both his eyes seem blind and merciless, and Arabel sobbed as his mouth closed on hers and she was pressed by his hardness into the deep softness of the bed.

She trembled, arched herself, and thrashed her legs in an effort to escape what was happening ... it overwhelmed her, the hot, seeking mouth and the hands that were no longer barred even by the silk. Words tumbled from his lips into her ears, from the mixed ancestry that was of the desert and the lush vales of Andalusia; a savage mixture of passion and poetry, and the exploration of her body that was both insistent and tormentingly exciting.

No, she sobbed, and felt the response she would have given her soul to repress ... hard muscles, skin like heated silk, an aching cry as fingers sank deep in her hair and his promise on the *mirador* was blasted into a thousand shimmering atoms.

'Hate you ...' she panted. 'Unforgivable ...'

'Hate me,' he breathed, his face buried in the tumbled silk of her hair. 'Right now I cannot care, *santina, querida*.'

Little saint . . . darling. Little fool! Fighting him on a small issue and losing out on a big one.

'I wish you in hell, Cortez . . .'

'Maybe,' he laughed softly. 'But at this moment I am in heaven.'

Sunlight spilled into the room, and with a little groan, hiding from that flood of gold, Arabel turned on her face and the warmth lanced across the bare skin of her shoulders. She turned her face just a fraction and saw the glimmer of peach silk on the floor beside the bed, and there swept over her in a tide of burning memory the feel of insistent lips, the caress of hands hardened by horse reins, the way that passionate Spaniard had done what he liked with her. There had been no way to stop him, and the shaming part was that she had not been able to hold out against the arousal of her own body . . . she stirred against the rumpled sheets and twisted about in a torment of self-accusation. She could have made of herself a thing of ice, a frigid block there in his arms, and then at least she could have thrown in his face that most hateful of all words . . . rapist.

But in all fairness it hadn't been like that, and she felt her cheeks grow hot as she remembered holding him . . . holding him as he took her with firm, thorough, sensuous strength. Now he had the laugh on her, and she could never forgive him for that. He had played on her innocence with all his own expertise, and he had even made the union so incredibly enjoyable that there had been barely a flicker of pain.

The *espada*, she told herself through gritted teeth, knowing exactly where to give the bull the kiss of steel right through the heart. A pang and then the paradise flooding in so that nothing mattered except that it should never end.

Arabel pummelled the pillow in its rumpled lace slip ... *I could kill him, kill him*, she thought wildly. *He had no right* ... except that he had every right. Her husband, with every legal sanction to indulge himself with her, getting from her everything he wanted, a fight, a passionate culmination, and possibly a child.

Devil take him, there would be no getting away from him if he had brought that off, for that was what he wanted above all, a son who would eventually take on San Devilla, this great spread of land and house which the Don had won for himself in the sun-hot arenas where death stalked in the guise of a sleek black bull. From the dark alleys of Seville he had made it to an *estancia* whose every acre, every tree and stone was absolutely his ... as she had been made his in the savage beauty of the Spanish night.

With a kind of grace and sweep and certainty of steel he had taken possession of her, leaving her this morning with just a few faint markings on her white skin, with tousled hair and slightly aching lips, and a kind of wonderment that what girls feared could be so—so natural and not in the least degrading.

Arabel lay there and thought about the way it had been ... why had it been like that? Was it at all possible that she wasn't a virgin and had been with a man before she had known Cortez?

A hand clenched against her heart and she felt a sensation of fierce rejection that she might in any way have been a cheap sort of girl ... it wasn't so much that she feared the Don's anger, but she just didn't like the idea that when she had worked in Venezuela she might have led a less than decent life. She probed for the answer behind that foggy veil that clouded her mind, but it just wouldn't reveal itself ... the only person who would know for sure would be Cortez himself, and she lay there rigidly and didn't want the day to advance any further, when she would have to see him face to face.

What would she see? A smile of triumph lurking about that well-cut mouth, or would a cold fury glitter in his eye because what he had was a wife who had let another man be first with her?

How his Spanish heart would hate that, and how his Spanish pride would find ways to punish her.

Suddenly her spine stiffened as he spoke behind her, having come unnervingly close to the bedside while she lay there lost in her confused thoughts. 'Coffee?' he drawled. 'You must be feeling parched, and we have a custom that the bridegroom waits on the bride in order to spare her blushes.'

'Have you left me any blushes?' she murmured, her heart beating fast against the bed. 'Could you put the cup on the side table—I'm not going to sit up, not right now.'

'Aren't you?' She heard him laugh softly to himself. A spoon shifted in a saucer as he placed the coffee on the table, but he didn't leave the bedroom as she hoped he would. He came into her line of vision and picked something up off the floor. 'The moment has come when this can be of use and ornament . . .'

Arabel shivered as fur brushed her bare skin, and still with her back to him she raised herself and allowed him to assist her into the bedjacket, which he drew around her with a sensuous slowness, pulling the little ermine tails over her soft curves. '*Demonio*,' he breathed. 'You are so bewitching that I feel disembowelled.'

'Ugh, Cortez, what a description!' She turned herself so that she was facing him, and she tried to maintain a scrap of poise in the sudden sight of his powerful darkness of skin and hair against the knee-length terrycloth robe that he wore. He had a masculine tautness and glow to him that was partly from his sauna, and partly from last night. She searched his face as she reached for her cup of coffee. Was it there, what she dreaded to find? Her lips felt dry as she sipped at the hot creamy liquid.

Suddenly he smiled, a brief flicker of lightness across the tanned darkness of his face, moving in and out of the claw-marks left by the hot southern sun.

'How are you?' he asked. 'You look fairly in one piece . . . that hair of yours, like Jason's fleece of gold, and that skin! Did I mark you? Did I—hurt?'

Her stomach muscles contracted at his look. 'You —you should know that,' she said constrictedly. 'You're more experienced than I am—aren't you?'

'Of course.' He sat down on the bedside and watched her intently. 'You hate me for forcing the citadel, eh? I am but a man, *chica mia.* I am no Pope, no chastising monk, and I don't think what happened was entirely to your dissatisfaction, not if I am any judge of a woman.'

'I'm sure your judgment of women is as expert as your judgment of bulls,' she rejoined.

'Some *corrida,*' his lip quirked into a grin. 'For my part of the game I liked what I held in my arms last night and I wasn't going to break your spirit, or mar that slim and lovely challenge of a body. Say it was good!'

'I—I'll be darned if I will!' Her eyes shimmered as they met his gaze. 'You made me—made me give in to you—but will you tell me something?'

'Anything at all,' he said amiably. 'Try me.'

'Was I—were you able to tell if I had ever—played around?' It was awful having to ask him such a question, but she needed desperately to know. 'You see how it is, *señor*, I just can't remember what has been personal to me and I think—yes, I'm sure that I knew a man before there was you. I—I believe I loved him. You believe it as well, don't you, that's why you—forced me.'

For at least a full minute he just sat there on the side of the bed with that black-lashed, dusky-gold eye so intent upon her face that it became like a drill touching a nerve, and she suddenly shivered and her fingers drew the fur tassels across her bosom ... the bosom his lean fingers had caressed last night, those same hands that had struck the *coup de grâce* for many a bull, and yet ... her fingers clenched the soft ermine tails, and her skin quivered. He had not hurt her ... why had he not hurt her?

Suddenly he leaned towards her and the triangular eye-patch made his good eye seem as piercing a sword. 'You can take my word for it, *chica*, you were *imaculata*, as we say in Spain. No convent girl was ever more innocent, no wine from a cloister was ever as sweet. Is that what is causing the concern, eh?'

'How can you be so—so sure?' She bit her lip, any semblance of composure shattering beneath his gaze.

'There was no wounding, eh?' He said it quite naturally, and as she shook her head she wouldn't let herself believe that she had glimpsed a strange flicker of tenderness across his hard face.

'I thought—how is it possible——?'

'If a man has regard as well as desire for a certain woman, he doesn't go at her like a bull at a barrier. That kind of behaviour is for unfledged boys and churlish, self-centred louts. Whatever you may think of me, *querida*, I have my standards, and I wouldn't cause any harm or hurting to something of mine which I happen to value.' His fingers moved and twined themselves in her silky hair, and only if she had jerked away from him would she have felt a tug of pain. She sat there tensely, as if mesmerised by what he was saying to her. 'Sometimes for a man, perhaps once in a lifetime, a girl is like a soft-nosed, spirited filly, and there is no need for spurs or whip if a man is sure of himself. It is only the unsure man, basically flawed with a selfish streak, who damages his woman in the act of making love to her for the first time, and whether or not you will say it, it was good, *guapa*, and there deep in your eyes is a little light, a sparkle of discovery—yes, my sweet, it is possible for a woman to enjoy herself with a man who knows about women.'

'And that really gives you a kick, doesn't it, *señor*, that you got under my skin with your Casanova tricks!' Resentment flared that it should be so, that with those firm lips and those sure hands he could draw forth from her a pulsating response that made a blush burn her body to the tips of her toes, which curled beneath the bedcovers at what he must be remembering of last night.

'Would it have pleased you better, Arabel, had I left you in bed this morning a broken, outraged woman, like something left on a battlefield? Would that have given you a real bone to chew on, a real cause to hate me?' A tiny muscle jerked at the side of his mouth, and holding her by the hair he drew her towards him. 'Would you have felt justified in hating me had I used you instead of loving you?'

'You—you don't love me,' she protested. 'You own me—you just said so, with your talk about not harming something that you value. I can be made use of, here in this room, and later on as part of your breeding herd!'

He laughed, very softly, when she flung that in his face. 'Exciting, honey-hot love, *bellisima esposa*, that between us we might give a child to the light, eh? How you tempt a man with your sweet face and your bitter words, and I won't deny that it would be a pleasure to make with you a black-haired *niño*, tough and tantalising because of the dash of pure ice in his warm southern bloodstream. Shall we set about it, here and now?'

'*No*,' she did jerk away and flinched at the tug on her hair roots. 'Haven't you had your fun?'

'The fun, *guapa*, has only begun.' His fingers slid out of her hair and with that swift, frightening sureness he had his arms around her and through her body shot the awareness that once again she would be helpless to resist him when those hard lips took hers. She twisted and turned her head in an effort to avoid the capture of her mouth, and he only laughed softly at her and she felt those lips elsewhere, pushing aside the white fur.

'Oh, someone might come in!' she gasped. 'Why aren't there locks on the doors?'

'Because, adorable prude, you are now in a Latin house and we don't regard *this* as something shameful.' *This* was a warm mouth that found nerve centres she hadn't dreamed about, soft swells and hollows that he burrowed into until everything was swooning torment.

'Cortez ... *please*——'

'I love it when you beg, *chica*, and it's my pleasure to oblige.' Warm, low laughter spilled into the hollow of her neck, and the sunlight blazed, shocking and splendid, down over the muscles of his back, striking against his brown skin where horn welts showed white as bone. There wasn't an ounce of superfluous fat on him; his muscles moved like oiled ropes under his warm, firm skin. His chest hair was sable and slightly rough against her white body ... no, she thought hazily, civilised men don't behave like this in bold daylight. This couldn't be happening ... but it was, and she was part of it, in the sure grip of powerful hands that lifted her close to that strong, scarred body and made her know him, the stranger who was her husband ... the devil who held a key to this unwanted heaven where she betrayed that other man who was lost to her in the past she couldn't recall.

This was now the reality, and Cortez was making very sure she shared the future with him.

Her hand clenched his shoulder, her widened eyes dwelt upon his face, and words trembled on her lips.

'What is it?' he murmured. 'Say it, *chica.* Don't hold back, unless you are going to tell me to go to hell again. I don't think I'd like that right now, when you look such an angel in my arms.'

'You—you look like a pirate,' she said. 'You give no quarter, do you, *señor espada*?'

'Why should I, my sweet? You won't give so I must take, and the good *Dios* knows that I only take what is *mine*.'

Mine ... he sank the word into the soft skin of her neck. 'Soon,' he whispered, 'it will be the *fiesta* of La Pasionaria and we'll go into the hills and have the saint bless us in the chapel. Would you enjoy that?'

'Does it matter what I enjoy?' Her breath fanned against his hard cheek and beneath her fingertips were the ridges of a horn scar deep in his muscled back. Her breath caught in her throat as she imagined the fierce pain of it and the reckless challenge which had driven him on, until that final blinding fight at Talavera. 'I very much doubt if I could share what you enjoy!'

'You can say that at this moment and really believe it?' He gave a short laugh. 'My obstinate one, I shall teach you to enjoy living my life if it's the last thing I do.'

'Aren't you tempting fate with that kind of talk?'

'Fate?' He lifted her gold hair against his face, a gesture utterly pagan, with the sunlight flinging its lance across the dark gold skin of his back. 'It's only you I want to tempt, my lovely child. Only you!'

'You take your pleasure, but don't you care, Cortez, that I have memories to unlock? You seem as if you want me like this, a foggy-minded doll in your arms, pliant and incurious about my life before you came into it!'

'That's the Arab in me,' he mocked. 'If I said I wanted it otherwise you wouldn't believe me, so be quiet, slave, and just let me kiss you.'

His mouth closed upon hers and the sunlight was lost behind the drowsy weight of her eyelids. She couldn't think any more, or question the truth of his statement. There was no conviction in her belief that he wanted her with a mind that was clear, with all the confusion swept away.

That mistiness was his shield, protecting him from the truth, this dark plunderer who carried her away on wings of passion.

CHAPTER TEN

How did she behave, Arabel asked herself, when she met his family at lunch and it became apparent that he had flung aside his patience and taken her for a real wife instead of one who merely bore his name? He had robbed her of more than her self, he had stripped away that cloak of privacy and that tiny sense of triumph because he was husband but not lover. Now a very drastic change had taken place and, with a thud of her heart, she saw that it showed.

She had just emerged from the shower and was seated on a stool in front of the dressing-table mirror. It was crazy, but there was a subtle difference in the look which the mirror gave back to her. Her eyes were inordinately blue and deep, and there was a flush of carnation over her cheekbones. She reached up a hand and touched her hair and it sprang live and silky from her brow. Since coming to San Devilla she hadn't concerned herself with her own looks, but now she had to admit that she wasn't exactly plain. That she had good skin and hair, and eyes not often seen in Andalusia, lay at the root of the Don's passion for her; they were the culprits that aroused the demon of desire in him.

She sat there in a blue wrapper and slowly drew a comb through her hair; the sunlight through the shutters followed the movements of the comb and there was a soft crackling sound as if her hair was alive with electricity. It had, she admitted, been like coming into contact with a magnetic charge and he had probably magnetised her so that in the future she would pick up Latin habits whether she wanted to or not, and the person she once had been would become more like the inhabitants of San Devilla.

He meant it to be that way! She was to be merged among his kin and his possessions, and he would rejoice if she never regained her lost memory ... never again had any recollection of that other man whose face and form, whose voice and touch eluded her as the tail of the lizard the jaws of the cat. Each time she glimpsed that shadowy image, the lithe figure of the Don obscured it.

He came into a room and his presence was too vital, too forceful, and somehow frightened away that shadow of a memory. Even as she reached out it was gone and she was left with a smouldering resentment against her husband for so imposing himself upon her that she couldn't come to grips with that other haunting figure.

She flung down the comb and dug her fingers into her hair, pressing them into her scalp as if to force those iron gates that kept back the dam where the facts of her former life bobbed about like so much flotsam, which would tell her so much if only she could grasp something solid.

'What is wrong, Arabel? Have you a headache?'

She glanced up dazedly and there was the face and figure of Luz reflected in the mirror. She turned round on the stool and forced a smile to her lips. 'No, as usual I'm trying to recapture my old self, the person I was before your cousin—married me.'

'Is it so important to know?' Luz leaned against the dressing-table and regarded Arabel with inquisitive eyes. 'Is it not enough to be the wife of Don Cortez, who owns all the land as far as the eye can see, and who can surely give a woman enough to think about without bothering her brain about things that are past? When one is young the future is all that counts, is it not?'

'For you, Luz, because you don't know how awful it is to have important matters blotted out as if they had never been—and I know they matter. They matter to me! There was someone——' Arabel broke off, biting her lip. 'I know you think that the sun rises and sets around the black head of your cousin, but I had a life of my own before he took over and if I do remember, and that someone is still alive and in need of me, then I shall go to him and Cortez can go to the devil for all I care! I'm just not going to pretend a mad passion for *him*, not to please any of you. Why should I?'

'Oh, there could be reasons.' Luz strolled over towards the great bed, still unmade and with unmistakable impressions in both sets of pillows that two people had shared it. The fine linen and lace was rumpled, and Luz was faintly grinning as she turned to look at Arabel.

'I knew he wouldn't spend many more nights alone, and you still talk about some other man? You must be *loca*!'

'There's more to life than what goes on in a bedroom,' Arabel said defiantly, the flush deepening in her cheeks nonetheless. 'Your cousin has plenty of muscle and nerve, and short of screaming the house down there wasn't much I could do about his—his invasion of my room. I harboured a fragile hope that he would behave like a gentleman, but he isn't one of those, is he? The alley cat doesn't change its ways just because it moves house, has a silk cushion to sit on and tenderloin for dinner.'

'The way you talk!' Luz said it almost with admiration. 'You have the edge to your tongue which some Latin women have, do you know that? Cortez wouldn't ask for honey on the tongue, he'd prefer a dash of pepper and spice.' Luz gave a laugh and ran her eyes over Arabel. 'You are now looking like a real woman and those shadows are gone from under your eyes and there is a glow under your skin. When we first met you we all wondered if Cortez had lost the sight of his other eye, for you seemed so washed-out and listless, not at all the kind of woman to attract him, especially as a wife. But suddenly you have come alive—is it that exciting with a man? I can't wait to find out!'

'You had better wait or Cortez will break your neck,' Arabel said, alarmed for the girl, who often rode alone among the *vaqueros*, some of whom were sun-dark and vibrantly lean as whips, with eyes that were wicked with Latin diablerie. They would respect the girl as the Don's female cousin, but not if she started making eyes at them, inquisitive about men and their ways, and aware that as a Latin girl she must wait for the head of the household to approve someone before she could be betrothed and married.

'And he'll break yours, Arabel, if you ever talk to him about running away to some other man. You must realise that you belong body and soul to Cortez?' Luz jingled the charms on her wrist. 'It strikes me as being exciting beyond words to belong so completely to a man such as Cortez, but you are a strange one, eh? Being foreign you like your independence, but Spain is a man's country and here a woman has to be subtle and seductive in order to get her own way.'

'The harem system,' Arabel said scornfully. 'Slave to a man's desires.'

'Did you truly find those desires so hard to endure?' Luz picked up from among the bedcovers the ermine bedjacket with its impudent tails. 'And look at what he gives you; you would be a fool, Arabel, if you really thought yourself so hard done by. The women I could name who would purr like cats to be in your shoes!'

'I expect I could name one myself,' Arabel rejoined. She went to the wardrobe and drew open the doors, and though it would have given her a certain satisfaction to have dressed herself in a trouser-suit, she had learned quite a lesson with regard to the bedjacket and didn't fancy a repeat performance and that devastating loss of self when Cortez had his way. She ran a hand along the selection of day and evening wear and supposed that she should be grateful for such lovely things. Many a working girl would have purred with gratitude, but added to his generosity was his merciless disregard for her state of amnesia. He didn't care a snap of the fingers that her mind was in a state of confusion; it was her body that he wanted, and now he had it, and these tasteful garments were meant to enhance what it gave him pleasure to possess.

Her lips took a pained twist as she drew forth a matching knife-pleated shirt and calf-length skirt in jade-blue silk. She dropped the wrapper and dressed herself, aware that Luz was watching her every movement with a Latin girl's intense curiosity about someone so different from herself.

Arabel stepped into T-strapped shoes softly lined with kidskin and in two subtle shades of blue, the open sides and slim heels setting off the slenderness of her ankles and legs. She returned to the mirror and swirled her hair into a silky conch-shell, fixing it with a clip.

'Your hair would look stunning fixed with tortoiseshell combs under a black lace mantilla,' Luz remarked. 'It is naturally that colour, a person can see that. Not like some of the tourist women on the beach, with their roots like the copper-green of unpolished jugs.'

'If I didn't look like this, dammit——' Arabel stared into her own eyes as she applied light-rose colour to her lips, not that they really needed it. The Don her husband had made sure that her mouth had a glow to it.

'You think Cortez is only interested in the way you look?' Luz casually opened a slim leather case that lay on the dressing-table, and instantly she caught her breath. 'Santa Maria, will you feast your eyes on these! Did he give them to you last night?'

Against the black velvet inside the case lay an exquisite double-heart brooch of diamonds and sapphires, and a pair of ear-studs of glittering divided hearts. Lovely, heart-melting, but they might have been beach pebbles for all Arabel cared as she gave them a scornful look. Her fingers curled and she wanted to snatch the case from Luz and hurl its contents out of the window.

'He's so accustomed to paying for his pleasures that he forgets I'm for free,' she said, gritting her teeth. Twin hearts joined by a tiny diamond arrow ... who did he think he was kidding?

'You really are *loca*.' Luz stood gazing into the jewel case with greedy eyes. 'Not to say naïve and foolish if you imagine that a Spaniard spends this kind of money on women who sell their favours ... in any case, whoever knew a matador who had to pay a woman to share his company! When a Spaniard gives jewels he is making an investment; his wife is his bank, and it also impresses those in the same line of business.'

'How very romantic!' Arabel took the case from Luz and snapped it shut. She flung it down on the dressing-table with a show of contempt that made her feel a little less like his bought thing ... she had to be that if other women he had known had not that kind of money spent on them.

'Spanish people are realistic,' said Luz, 'and you had better accept what is real and forget what you may never remember.'

'I—I have to remember.' Arabel clenched her hands together and felt again that sense of being trapped within the unbreakable strands of a Spanish marriage, condemned to endure life at San Devilla without ever knowing what it might be like to be loved by that other man whom she had lost and might never see again. To remember him would be something of far more value to her than a diamond brooch with hearts locked together in a mockery of love.

'Cortez should have married a woman of his own sort,' she said. 'Riva Montelegre would have suited him better.'

'I find you very hard to fathom,' said Luz, shaking her smooth dark head and looking at Arabel with eyes that were puzzled and a little apprehensive. 'You won't even try on the brooch and see how it looks, and that is the first thing a normal person would do——'

'But I'm not in my normal mind,' Arabel said bitterly. 'I've lost my memory and I'm shut off from a recollection of the people I've known and loved. It's all part of a person's character, what has made her, and I can't behave as if it doesn't matter that half of me is in shadow—as if I only started to exist when Cortez came boldly into that prison and brought a priest with him. He took advantage of me when I was least able to defend myself, and I won't forgive him for that, nor be grateful for his darned jewels. Let him put them in the family vault if they're only an investment that's meant to impress his business rivals!'

Arabel walked back and forth as she spoke, the pleated blue silk falling gracefully about her slender figure. She was unaware of how striking she looked in the beautifully cut two-piece, with a proud tilt to her fair head and a smouldering quality to her eyes. She was restless with nervous energy, tensed up to endure the family luncheon that lay ahead of her, the cynosure of all those knowing glances . . . how could it be avoided when the servants would have whispered the news that Don Cortez had brought his foreign bride to heel and would no longer spend his nights austerely alone!

'This place is positively feudal,' she exclaimed. 'A sort of castle filled with the Don's retainers who bow and scrape to him as if their very lives depend on his good humour. Lord of the manor! Self-made despot in his very own kingdom, who won't be satisfied until he has me waddling around like a pregnant cow!'

'You will never waddle, my dear, but will look charming even in that interesting state,' drawled a deep voice from the doorway. Arabel swung round and there was her husband clad in a magenta shirt and dark grey trousers, lines of sardonic amusement deep in his face. 'See how she blushes, Luz? She burns in a fire of self-inflicted torment, and why she feels tormented is very much a mystery when she has certainly learned that I admire every particle of her.'

'This?' Arabel swept a contemptuous hand down her silk-clad figure, hating him for mocking her in front of his Spanish cousin. 'Skin and bone and a hank of blonde hair!'

'Gold,' he cut in. 'Golden flames, my love, and why the devil should I not delight in having you? By the saints, I only wish I could enjoy the sight of you with two eyes instead of one!' As he said this his brows came together, densely black above the good eye and the blind one. 'I have only the memory of how devastating a truly pretty woman can look to a man who hasn't had an eye gouged out.'

'That was your own fault—entirely your own,' Arabel cried. 'There was no need for you to fight any more, but you couldn't pass up the challenge, could you? You had your farm and security from ever being poor again, but it was at Talavera that Joselito made his last stand, wasn't it?'

There her words broke off and she gazed at him with a stunned look on her face. 'Why—what made me say that?' she murmured. 'Who is Joselito?'

'He was one of Spain's greatest matadors, perhaps her finest.' Don Cortez spoke the words very quietly, and his lean body in the silk shirt and dark trousers had a swordstick tension about it. 'You have no doubt heard him spoken of here in Spain; he died at Talavera where I lost my eye, and as you say, Arabel, it was my own fault. Why should a woman feel sympathy for that?'

'I don't,' she said, but somewhere inside her there was a strange ache, as if for a brief moment it had hurt her that one of those keen eyes should have been torn from that lean face, leaving a gaping hole that spouted blood on the black and silver fighting suit. 'The risk was hardly worth the prize, *señor*, a tail and a pair of ears for half your sight for the rest of your days.'

'Pepper-tongued, is she not, Luz? We might yet make a worthy *duena* out of her.' He took a sudden stride to Arabel and had her left hand at his lips before she could stop him. She felt his mouth against her skin and the deep-seated nerves twisted inside her and the feeling was so acute that she had to wrench away from him, dragging her hand from the warm pressure of his lips.

'Shy, my dear?' he mocked, but his hand clenched at his side and the knuckles gleamed like ivory through the tanned skin. His glance raked the blue two-piece and settled on the soft swell of her bosom. 'I left something for you and I'd like you to wear it——'

'This, cousin *mio*?' Luz, with mischief in her eyes, picked up the leather jewel case which Arabel had flung down among the toiletries. Luz handed him the case and he flipped it open, studied the brooch a moment, and then removed it from its velvet bed. It gleamed white-fire and blue in his fingers, and then quite deliberately he attached it to the silk of her shirt so that she felt the brush of his fingers against her body. Again she felt that sensuous reaction deep inside her, and her resentment of it blazed in her eyes as she looked up at him.

'Very pretty,' he murmured. 'Significant, eh, two hearts joined as one over the heart of my wife?'

'Doubtless your idea of a joke,' she said coldly. 'Your heart and mine have about as much in common as a rabbit and a rattlesnake.'

'What a woman!' he jibed, shaking his black head. 'Not a murmur of thanks for a charming trinket I had especially made for you?'

'What am I supposed to do, to be so honoured?' she asked. 'Give you a sweeping curtsey and touch my brow to your generous hand?' With an air of disdain she fitted action to her words, and all the time she felt the dangerous tension in his lean body, the almost palpable beat of anger in his veins, then suddenly his hand was gripping her elbow and strong fingers felt as if they might crush her bones.

'Let us go down and have some food,' he said curtly. 'It would seem that an empty stomach is having an odd effect upon your imagination.'

He marched her to the doorway and Luz followed them, saying with honey-toned sweetness: 'If this is married bliss, then I think, cousin, that I shall settle for the convent.'

'Luz,' he gave a brief laugh, 'you are too much a Latin woman to be content with a life of chastity. I think it is this wife of mine who should be enrolled in the cloisters.'

'The sooner the better as far as I'm concerned,' Arabel informed him. 'Anything would be better than having to endure your arrogance!'

His fingers gripped and as flesh and bone protested, she felt driven to a further reckless impulse there at the head of the stairs. 'You can't join my heart to yours even if you're strong enough to overcome me in—other ways. My heart is mine to give, or to keep, and no matter how hard you try, Don Cortez, you won't make an adoring slave out of me! I may not remember much about my past life, but one thing I'm very sure of is that I'm what they call a one-man woman. I feel it right at the marrow of my bones, and I know that no man—no other man, *señor*, is ever going to replace that man I knew before I woke up to find myself married to you!'

He stared down at her, there above the curving sweep of the iron-balustraded stairs, and there was a brilliant, penetrating flame burning at the centre of his golden eye. It pierced through her, savage, primitive, demanding, so that for a timeless moment the hot sands of the desert seemed to sweep over her in a golden *sirocco*, and the untamed pain of the *tortura* seemed to bend and rack her. It was unendurable and she had to get away from what he unleashed in that breathless moment as they stood eye to eye.

'Let ... me ... go!' Her words rang out, and the curving well of the stairs made an echo chamber that picked them up and flung them like a cry of agony against the mosaic tiles of the arcaded hall. Uncaring if he broke her arm Arabel twisted away from him, wincing at the pain and feeling a slim heel of her shoe turn over as she teetered very close to the top stair.

She flung out her other hand towards his face, or was it his shoulder? She didn't really know, except that she was suddenly off balance and on the verge of plunging downstairs. He abruptly pushed her backwards and she stumbled and went down on her knees, gripping the iron of the staircase, holding fast to it as her heart thudded with alarm and her knee-bone stung.

It all happened in a matter of seconds ... she saw him towering above her, almost like a figure of doom, and then he was falling backwards and she heard the thuds that his body made as he fell down and down that long hard curve of stairs, having lost his balance in that split moment of pushing her out of danger.

Even as a sobbing scream broke from her she heard someone cry out: 'You've killed him, you stupid little fool! You—I could kill you!' Hands slapped Arabel twice across the face, stingingly, and the young face of Luz was torn with fright and anger a moment before she raced downwards to where Cortez now lay still in the bend of the stairs.

It felt like a nightmare, and even the slaps had left her numb and unbelieving. She knelt there and felt unable to move as people ran from various parts of the house and collected about the ominous stillness of that figure which Arabel had never seen other than active with life and purpose.

They blotted him out, those people who cared for him, and their Spanish voices came in strange waves to her ears ... just as in a nightmare she had no control over what was happening and there wasn't a whimper of protest in her when someone took her by the arm and led her back to her room. Someone spoke and she was vaguely aware that she was to stay here, like a child who had badly misbehaved, and she was to leave to others what had to be done in the matter of her injured husband.

'Injured?' She clutched at an arm and saw dazedly the face of his friend, the one who had smiled and not looked so terribly grim when he had started to teach her how to play the guitar. 'Oh—how badly?'

'We don't yet know,' he said, and he began to walk away from her.

'I—I have to go to him,' she tried to pass him in the doorway, but he blocked the way.

'No.' He shook his head. 'Cortez is unconscious and there is nothing you can do. A doctor has been sent for and you would only be in the way, *señora.*'

'But—I'm his wife,' she said. 'It's my right——'

'Is it?' he asked, and he gave her a long, serious look.

'This—this isn't the bullring,' she cried out. 'You can't carry him off and stitch him up and have no women present but the nuns—this is San Devilla and he's my husband!'

'Good of you to remember that, *señora.*' His friend looked sardonic, but his eyes were bleak, as if he knew something terrible about that fall on the stairs which she was not to be told about.

'It's a conspiracy,' she whispered, 'you're all going to keep me from seeing him and I have to know if he's going to be all right. It's uncivilised, cruel, what you're doing to me!'

'It's the sensible thing,' he said firmly. 'You will be informed as soon as we know ourselves how bad the damage is——'

'Damage?' Her fingernails dug into the masculine arm. 'His back has been hurt, hasn't it? He toppled backwards, halfway down those hard stairs and struck his spine—and it's my fault! Mine!'

'Yes,' came the grim reply, 'Luz tells us that you pushed him.'

She was left alone after that, to stare numbly at the walls of this room where last night and this morning Cortez had been vibrant with life and dominance.

'But I didn't push him,' she whispered to herself.

'But you argued with him,' came back the answer in the chambers of her shocked mind. 'You called him arrogant, you said that anything would be better than having to stay with him ...'

And that anything could be a broken spine that would cripple him, and no more would he ride his land like a *vaquero*, and make a woman know him from her tingling toes to her swooning eyes.

Arabel slithered down against the side of the great bed and buried her face in the covers that still held a vagrant aroma of his tobacco and his warm skin. Her fingers gripped and clenched where he had lain, laughing softly, tauntingly, as she struggled with him to no avail at all. It wasn't only his strength which had conquered her; in that final, tumultuous surrender she had been as much a part of that primitive rite as he had been, white limbs bound to sun-dark ones in a sweet-wild journey out of herself into the bloodstream and sinews of another human being.

It should have been enough for her. For him it was enough because he was a man, but still she craved for what he had snatched her away from—the face and the form of that someone who lay waiting in her subconscious to be resurrected by the return of her memory.

Physical pleasure couldn't be measured against her wild certainty that she had loved someone with an intensity almost beyond bearing ... but if Cortez was crippled by that fall then she would never be able to leave him, even if one day she remembered the man she had to think of as his rival.

It was untrue what Luz had said, for she hadn't pushed him, and wouldn't have dreamed of doing so. But she had quarrelled with him at the head of the stairs and that had led to his downfall. But for that he wouldn't now be desperately hurt, perhaps never again to overwhelm a woman with his power and grace and self-determination.

CHAPTER ELEVEN

It might have been one or two hours later that a maid brought a tray of food and coffee to Arabel. She had lost track of time and was surprised to find herself out on the balcony of the big bedroom, crouched in a cane chair like a small girl hiding from adults who were unforgivingly angry with her.

The maid placed the tray on the cane table, neither looking at Arabel nor speaking to her. She had obviously been given orders not to say anything. The foreign girl was to be punished. She had caused Cortez to have his accident, and this was the deep, almost primitive south where young wives were at the mercy of the matriarchs; the mothers of men who felt their power and used it. The Don's aunt was one of those, and never for a moment had she been pleased that her nephew had married someone so different from themselves.

'How is my husband?' Arabel pleaded of the maid, but her answer was a shrug of the shoulders and a look that said plainly that she was an outcast in this house, and the good *Dios* help her if Don Cortez didn't rally from that fall and soon regain his former strength and power.

'Has the doctor arrived?' Arabel gazed at the girl with begging eyes, so intensely blue that the contours of her face seemed bruised by their anguish. 'Please, I must be told something or I shall go crazy!'

'The medico and his nurse are here, *señora.*' The maid spoke in a chilly voice. 'Please to eat your food while it is hot, and don't bring the tray downstairs, for I shall fetch it.'

'Are they going to take the *señor* to hospital—tell me!'

'I cannot say, *señora.* He has been placed in a room on the ground floor, and that is all I am able to tell you.'

'Everyone blames me, don't they?' Arabel took a shaky breath. 'I blame myself, but I don't think I deserve this kind of treatment. Cortez himself wouldn't put me through this torture—he'd want me there at his side! I just know he would!'

'It doesn't always do for the foreigner to be sure of our Spanish way of thinking,' the maid replied, giving Arabel a cold, dark look. 'We aren't a soft people who forgive and forget easily, and here at the *estancia* we are all beholden to Don Cortez for a secure life, with good food to eat, work for the men, and someone who listens to our troubles when we have them and does his best to put them right. You are only a haughty foreign girl who has no love in her heart as we feel it.' The Spanish girl beat her hand against her breastbone to make her words even more emphatic. 'You are like a pretty schoolgirl, unfit for marriage with a real man like the *dueno*, but men have their heads turned, and that is always the devil's work.'

Having said this, having dared to go so far because the *dueno* lay stricken and his foreign wife was in severe disgrace, the maid withdrew from the balcony and left Arabel alone and tormented, cut off from the drama below stairs, and from the medical verdict on that hurt body which had been so vital with life and pleasure only a few short hours ago.

A shudder went through Arabel and though the hot sun struck the balcony where she sat she felt as if someone had stabbed her with a shaft of ice and it was dripping down her spine and spilling round into her groin. She pressed her hands to herself and gave an aching groan. She wanted to be with him, to smooth back his black hair from his unaware face, and be there when he opened his eyes so she could beg him to believe that it had never been her wish to see him fall as if down a black pit, his flesh and bone thudding endlessly against those stairs.

The sun struck a gleam against the coffee pot and she realised that it would be foolish and of no help to Cortez to let herself grow weak from lack of nourishment. He'd ask for her when he came around from his fall; he'd need her, as he had last night, and she would require the strength to fight his family when they tried to stop her from being with him.

With a shaking hand she poured coffee and slopped it in the saucer; she didn't add cream but took it strong and black and very sweet. After a few minutes it helped to steady her nerves, and she forced herself to eat the vegetable omelette, and then the caramel custard. She ate them without any awareness of what they tasted like, forcing down each mouthful, banking up her strength, acutely aware of the isolation and quietness of her balcony. How cruel the Spanish could be, she thought. People of the *tortura*, lovers of the bullfight, who punished with the iron garotte.

She felt as if it were clamped about her throat, gripping and throttling her until suddenly her eyes were filled with tears. She pressed a napkin hard against her lips and stumbled over towards the balcony rail. She gazed through tear-blinded eyes at the courtyard below, where the palms and the flowers made a blur of dazzling colour, and where in the night she had often caught the sound of booted feet tramping back and forth, as if a memory tormented Cortez as much as its evasion tormented her.

What if his spine was badly damaged? The high leather boots would stand unused, and his pair of Arabs would grow fat in the stables for lack of exercise. She wouldn't see Cortez leap from the red saddle and caress the satiny flanks of the bay or the black, making the horse dance with animal pleasure at the touch of his hand.

Her teeth bit the napkin to hold back a whimper of sharp pain. She wanted to rush downstairs, to fling aside those people who barred her from his bedside, to see for herself if he was going to be cut off from all the things he so enjoyed ... his land, his bulls ... his woman.

She quivered from head to foot, remembering the way he had rubbed his face in her hair, nostrils flaring at its fragrance, a deep well of foreignness in him going back and down into the distant past, with attitudes and desires linked to desert forebears. She had been frightened by all that in him, and yet at the same time it had been acutely exciting.

It would be cruel ... unbearably cruel if because of her he was condemned to a wheelchair. She had never asked for that, nor wanted him laid low and prideless. Never! Never! But it had probably happened and now his family would torture her for it. Keep her away from him while they attended to his poor hurt body, and went in their black mantillas to the chapel to pray for his recovery.

The afternoon waned and dusk crept over the grounds of San Devilla. She heard the men riding in from the grasslands, but her straining ears had caught no sound of an ambulance, which meant that they were keeping Cortez here at the *estancia*, a sign that he was either too hurt to be moved just yet, or he was badly knocked about but likely to be on his feet again before too long.

It had to be the latter! It had to be, or she'd go quietly out of her mind confined up here like some prisoner awaiting her sentence.

Night fell and the maid on evening duty brought her a dinner tray. This was an older woman and one who was even less communicative; she removed the silver plate covers and dourly ignored Arabel's inquiry as to how the Don was. Was he conscious? Was he comfortable?

'In God's name tell me!' Arabel leapt to her feet and looked so wildly unhappy that the woman stared at her a moment, and then hastened away as if in fear of what the desperate girl might do to her. Arabel couldn't stand this another moment. She ran from the balcony through the rooms of the suite and out on to the gallery. When she reached the stairs she came to a sharp halt and stared down them, seeing it all again in her imagination, hearing the words flung back and forth, feeling that sudden shove that sent her to her knees, watching in horror as he went off balance and plunged backwards down the staircase.

Someone stood at the foot of the stairs watching her ... a lean dark figure of a man, his white shirt faintly gleaming under the hall lamps.

'Cortez ...!' She snatched at the sides of her skirt and went racing down to that lean figure, who as she neared him shifted a little more into the light. She saw his face, and her lifted heart sank down again.

'It is I, Juan,' he said. 'You should have stayed in your room, Arabel. My mother is very angry with you——'

'I have to know about Cortez!' She clutched at his arm, biting him with her fingernails but not aware of it. 'I have a right to know, and you aren't so cruel that you'll not tell me. At least tell me how he is, Juan.'

'He regained consciousness a couple of hours ago,' Juan said quietly, as if keeping down his voice in case his mother should hear and stop him from putting Arabel a little out of her misery. 'He's a mass of bruises, as you can imagine—why did you push him, Arabel? What got into you?'

'I didn't——' She gazed up at him, her blue eyes wild with denial. 'Luz must have been mistaken, or she said it deliberately to—to make you all hate me. How could I push him? He's far too strong and could crush me in his two arms if he wished. M-my shoe twisted over and I was tottering up there and as he pushed me back on to firm ground he seemed to lose his own balance. Juan, it's the truth, and I must know if he's going to be all right. There would be no justice if he came to more harm ... even the loss of an eye can't be compared with the loss of his mobility. He will walk? His spine—it is only badly bruised?'

'Shockingly bruised, and the doctor won't be entirely satisfied with his condition until he can be X-rayed. But he's being kept quiet and still overnight and will probably go to the hospital tomorrow——'

'Can I see him, Juan?' Her eyes were huge and pleading in her white face, little shadows intensified by the mysterious lighting of the Moorish lamps. A moth wafted its wings against a wall and somewhere in the garden a bird wailed a broken note. 'You'll let me see him, won't you? I'll be as quiet as a mouse—*please*.'

'I daren't.' He looked almost as unhappy as she did. 'Whatever happened up there, the two of you were arguing, and you know as well as I do that it would take a hell of a lot of anger and distraction to make a matador like Cortez lose his balance. You will just have to be satisfied with what I tell you, Arabel. He seems not too desperately injured, but we can't be absolutely sure——'

'Has he spoken to anyone?' She swallowed drily. 'Has he mentioned—me?'

'My mother has been with him, alone. He might have said something to her.'

'She hates me, doesn't she?' Arabel, feeling a sudden faintness, leaned back against one of the hall pillars, the tiling striking cool through the silk of her shirt. That morning the two-piece had been immaculate, but now it was creased, and there were coffee stains from the cup that had shaken in her unsteady hand. Her hair was loosened to her shoulders, and there were tear smudges on her face. She could feel Juan staring at her, and she knew that he was unable to decide if her fear was for herself or her husband. These people were direct and also complex. Love was love, and all she had shown was a petty disinclination to want nothing of Cortez but her release from what she considered a bondage rather than a marriage. They knew all about it, for a Latin house was a hive of gossip and barely suppressed interest in the marital problems of the *dueno* and his bride. They were well aware that last night he had made a proper wife of her, and now they were all saying that she had retaliated by pushing him down the stairs in the hope of putting an end to any more lovemaking.

Her eyes burned big and blue, making her face seem very fragile in its fine boning, and the reserve they took for a cold lack of passion.

'I know how bad it looks, between Cortez and me,' she said huskily. 'I wanted him to make allowances for this amnesia of mine, to let me remember—oh, it's all so mixed-up and flawed, this marriage of ours. He could have got me out of that prison without marrying me—he forced me into it, knowing things I've forgotten, that there was someone else in my life. Wasn't I supposed to resent that kind of high-handed treatment?'

'I don't really know, Arabel.' Juan shrugged his shoulders. 'It seemed to us that he did the best thing possible for you, in the circumstances. They might have taken you out and shot you for a spy.'

'But I'm an American citizen,' she exclaimed. 'They couldn't do that!'

'They've done it to others,' he said. 'Cortez couldn't take the chance that they wouldn't shoot you as well——'

'As well?' she took him up. 'Who did they shoot?'

'The two students. Didn't you know, Arabel? Didn't Cortez tell you?'

'No.' She shook her head dumbly. 'No, because it's highly likely that he knew one of them was—important to me.' The pieces of jigsaw were slipping into place, she thought tiredly. It was one of those young men who had meant such a lot to her, but his face was blank and there wasn't the faintest echo in her mind of his voice and the things that men whispered to a woman loved. Gone, she thought ... gone out of mind, a slumped figure against a blood-splashed wall and nothing more.

'I'm so worn out,' she put a hand against her forehead and suddenly swayed where she stood. Juan instantly reached out and caught hold of her, lifting her as her legs gave way and carrying her swiftly across to the *sala*. He went inside with her and laid her down on the big leather couch, pushing a cushion behind her head, which felt as if it were spinning round and would fly off into dark space.

'Lie quiet and I'll fetch you a drop of cognac,' he said, his voice gone soft and sympathetic. 'Poor little Arabel, so confused and misunderstood, and so like a small girl lost. Lie still, and please don't swoon!'

He hastened to the drinks cabinet and as in a distance she heard the clink of glassware, and felt a draining weakness in her body. He came back, placed an arm about her and lifted her so she could take small sips at the strong brandy in the big bowl. It made her ache that someone should be kind after this long day of misery, and as her throat blocked up she gave a choking sound and pushed the brandy bowl away from her lips.

'I—I can't——'

'You must, *guapa*.' His eyes were dark, tender as velvet as he wiped a spill of brandy from the side of her mouth. 'Pretty little lost girl, and Cortez can be damned overwhelming ... here, sip it quietly and get back your strength.'

As she obediently sipped she felt him stroking her hair, and it was so good that someone should be gentle with her after all those hours of punishing silence, of picturing Cortez with a broken back, of not being allowed to see that lean dark face stamped with high pride and nerve, the blind eye sealed off behind its black patch, like a secret locked away.

'You're a nice boy, Juan,' she murmured. 'Cortez was never like you, was he, except in a slight family resemblance when he was your age? His life never held much tenderness, did it? It was kill or be killed.

I can't say I blame your mother for refusing to let you take up the *capote*. It's such a cruel game.'

'It has many shades of meaning for Spanish people, and it pays well the successful matador.'

'And you aren't interested in that sort of success, are you, Juan? You want a normal existence, with none of the ambition and adulation that turn a man into a kind of devil who can't resist a challenge; a man a woman has to be afraid for, so much so that in the end she runs away.'

Juan gazed at her with a tinge of puzzlement in his eyes. 'You speak as if you knew what it felt like to be in love with such a man ... a man driven by a devil, as most matadors are until something happens to bring them to their senses.'

'Cold death in the hot afternoon,' she said, like a dreamer talking. 'Or something very close to it, like Cortez at Talavera, having to kill through a red mask, a satin horror in the sunlight, streaming as the crowd shrieked and stamped like barbarians, and applauded him as if it were truly a game and not sheer blinding agony that he wasn't going to show anyone, not if it struck him dead there on the sand. And he knew I watched him! He knew I was there, though I'd said I wouldn't be! He knew how I hated it and had begged him not to fight any more. I pleaded, wept, and no quarrel was ever like that one——!'

There, at that point, utterly stunned by what she was saying, Arabel broke off and gazed in sheerest bewilderment into the startled eyes of Juan. A long, long moment of discovery ticked away, palpable as the beating of her heart, and then a voice spoke from the other end of the room, angrily:

'You will let go of that woman this instant, do you hear me, Juan? She's a wicked, ungrateful, silly girl, and I won't have you falling under the spell of her white skin and gold hair, like that besotted fool of a man in the next room!'

'Mother!' Juan let go of Arabel as if her slim figure had turned to a flame and burned his fingers. He scrambled to his feet and stood looking at the slight, outraged figure of his parent as if he had been caught doing something disgraceful. 'Arabel was feeling unwell and I was giving her some cognac—she is very light-headed, for she's been saying the strangest things.'

'No doubt she has.' Señora Armendaz came further into the room, and mixed with the anger in her eyes was an undoubted look of strain. Arabel saw it and felt a clutch at her heart; she knew the woman cared for Cortez and had been with him for hours. How Arabel envied her those hours, but she wasn't going to extend the punishment ... not any more, not if Arabel had to push her out of the way in order to get to that besotted fool who lay next door.

'I'm going to him!' She jumped to her feet and weakness had given way to blazing resolve. 'You can't keep me out of that room any longer, *señora*. I know you mean well, but I also know that he wants me!'

'*Ay*, wants you,' the woman agreed cynically, shaking her head in its strip of lace. 'I've been begging and praying of him to send you away. I've tried my hardest to convince him that your foreign ways will never blend with his, but he refuses to listen to me. There is none so blind as a man in love! None so deaf to good advice. Cortez has done everything possible for you, but in return you have given him ingratitude and a lot of foolish arguments. You deserve to be sent away, and if I had my way——'

'You'd throw me out on my ear,' Arabel said, with a little twist of a smile. 'It would only be what I deserved, but I didn't know, you see, I didn't dream how much he meant to me!'

She didn't know what carried her from the *sala*, it could have been wings rather than wobbly legs, but no one was going to stop her from getting to the side of that man, no longer a shadow that kept moving in and out of the forceful body of Cortez Ildefonso. The two were one, and the shock of his fall had suddenly worked its miracle and as she went towards the bed where he lay she felt only the confusion of a bride who madly loved what lay there looking at her.

He held out a hand and with a deep sob she ran to him, knelt there and smothered his fingers with tears and kisses. 'Darling ... dearest ... mad, mad fool, why didn't you ever say? Why didn't you tell me? Why did you let me act the idiot and actually believe there could be anyone but *you*?'

Her eyes filled themselves with his rather wan face, and she put out a hand and tenderly touched his bruised temple. 'They kept me away from you and it's been hell on earth—*querido mio*, how do you feel? Are you terribly battered and b-broken?'

'All the better for seeing your dear, silly face,' he murmured, touching her cheek where the tears clung. 'I didn't realise they were keeping you forcibly away from me. Amita told me that you didn't wish to see me——'

'Oh, what a lie!' Arabel looked aghast. 'First Luz, telling them I pushed you down the stairs, and now your aunt making up that unkind story. Do they hate me so much?'

'They believe you—hate me!' he said, his eye intent upon her white, wet face. 'What has happened, *chica*? Has some of it come back to you?'

She nodded and reached forward hungry arms to cradle him. 'Am I hurting you?' she whispered.

He grinned a little. 'We seem always to be saying that to one another! No, my love, you might stab at times, but I have always known deep in my gut that you still cared for me. You do, eh?'

She snuggled his head against her, stroking him, tears spilling as she kissed his temple. 'Cortez, why didn't you shake it out of me? And your patience—you—all those weeks with me in the next room! In the old days you'd have——' She stopped and blushed deeply. 'What stopped you, until last night?'

'Sheer funk,' he admitted. 'I at least had you here and I didn't dare force the issue unless I did something that might permanently damage your mind. But last night—by the good *Dios*, when I touched you in that peachy thing it was all up with me and I had to have you, come what may. It was sheer glory, but I paid for it today, eh? *Demonio*, those stairs were like whips against my back——'

'Oh, don't!' She gave a whimper and pressed her hand against his lips. 'I can't bear to remember it—I thought you were dead or crippled. Are you going to be all right, *querido*? What did the doctor say?'

'He thinks I'll live—and love.' The smile deepened and Arabel gave a shiver of purest pleasure as his lips moved softly against the skin of her throat. 'Always, Arabel, never a moment when I stopped loving you and longing for you. I raged through every bar in Seville and Madrid after you left me and they put that damned patch over my eye. I wanted you! Grand God, did a man ever want a woman as I wanted you, but I allowed pride to stand in my way until I couldn't stand it a moment longer. Then when I got to Venezuela, where you had returned to work for Emanuel, I discovered that you had got yourself in dire trouble with the authorities by allowing a pair of fire-raisers to hide in your apartment—why in the name of the devil did you do that?'

'One of them knew I was an American working for a Spaniard in the city, and they came knocking on my door late at night. They were out of their wits with fear and neither of them was more than twenty. I—I couldn't turn them away, and now Juan tells me that they were shot.' She gave a sigh, and it was strange to be let in at last on all that had seemed so mysterious. The shock of seeing Cortez fall had opened her mind as if a key had turned, but there were still a few minor blanks and one of them was very puzzling.

'Cortez, how did we meet?' she asked.

He was silent a moment, and then he softly laughed. 'You worked in Venezuela for an acquaintance of mine, a man very fond of the *corrida*, who when he came to Spain on business brought with him his very cool and efficient American secretary. He introduced us, and suddenly before my eyes I saw coolness melt into devastating warmth when you smiled at me for the very first time. Ah, my very own Arabel, don't you yet know that for us it was love the moment our eyes met? It was heart leaping at heart, my blood-beat pounding in tune with yours, an instant recognition of the only woman for the only man. We didn't have to speak with words, our eyes spoke for us, and at that time I had a pair of eyes and they ate you from the crown of your golden head to the sweet hollows in your ankles.'

He drew a little away from her and drew her eyes to his face. 'You may not have remembered me with your mind when I made love to you, *adorada*, but your body answered to mine like the bell-flower to the honey-bee, sweet to madness, made to be mine, ever and always mine, and I'd have kept you here whether or not you remembered that in the summer when I lost my eye, we met and knew each other, and fell hopelessly in love.'

'And I walked out on you,' she said, stroking his face. 'I sent you a letter and flew away from you, believing I'd never meet you again.'

'I have that letter still,' he said, a brief grimness outlining his jaw. 'I can quote it from memory. "The bullfight is the love of your life," you wrote to me. "The adulation of the crowd and the ears and tail of your slain bull. I am not enough for you. No woman could ever fill all those seats at the *corrida*. Don't follow me! Leave me alone to get on with my life without having to compete with all the pomp and symbolism of your life as a matador. I thought I could cope with it, but I find I can't. Seeing you gored like that was too much for my nerves to take, let alone my innards and my heart. I couldn't live with it, dear as you are to me, exciting as I find you, much as I want to be in your arms. I have need of a husband, not a hero. I need to have you altogether or not at all. I need security, not the uncertainty of seeing you down there in the arena, Harlequin playing with death as if it were a game of cards. I love you too much to live in the shadow of what always lurks at the shoulder of the matador. *Adios*, and may the gods take care of you."'

'That was your letter to me, Arabel, just after I had lost my eye and you ran out on me. I was bitter, but gradually I began to realise the truth in what you had written to me.' He slowly, tenderly raised her face and pressed a kiss against her softly parted lips. 'Ah, Arabel, it hasn't been easy for either of us, but from now on—*demonio*, damn to perdition these bruises! How can I make love to you?'

She laughed and twined her arms about his neck. 'Tomorrow you get X-rayed, *querido mio*, and we make very sure you are going to be all right before any more battles of delight go on in that bedroom of ours. Oh, but what a little horror I've been to you! Why didn't you wring my neck?'

'Because, my pepper and spouse, I knew what you believed, that you had given your heart to someone else and you felt you betrayed him when you found it so deliciously satisfying in my arms. You were being loyal to *me* in the strangest way imaginable, and I couldn't say anything. I had to let you find me again all by yourself, and thanks to heaven you did. Like what you found, *mi vida*? Do I suit you, for by the saints you most certainly suit me!'

How much they suited each other was fully demonstrated a few weeks later at the *fiesta* of La Pasionaria, when the country people watched with keen and smiling eyes as the *dueno* of San Devilla strolled about the market fair with his young wife clinging to his arm. She wore a local costume, long-skirted, with penny-sized blue dots, frilled sleeves and more frills cascading from the hips. She looked graceful and supremely fulfilled, with a creamy carnation tucked in her golden hair. Her husband wore a wide Cordoban hat, a finely frilled *guayavera* shirt, tight-waisted dark trousers and short jacket. They looked as if welded together by a total understanding, a kind of mutual bliss in each other's company. Her eyes were brilliant as flowers, gazing up at him as if at the sun. Her feet seemed barely to touch the ground, as if she were a bright falcon on the wrist of her master.

Everything in their garden was dove-song and pepper-trees, and even the aunt had been won over, as everyone knew.

Especially since the news had got about that a twinkle in the eye of Ildefonso had become a certainty in the shape of a coming child . . . then would the sky be lit up with celebration rockets and the guitars would go mad with love song.

They paused at a stall selling the odds and ends that hopeful vendors bring to the fair, and Arabel leaned forward to study a buckle with a bull's head engraved upon it. 'May I treat you to a memento of a happy day, *señor*?' She took the buckle into her slender fingers. 'It will look quite dashing on your belt once I've given it a polishing.'

'Like the sword?' he murmured, his arm firmly about her waist, which hadn't yet lost its slimness. 'The one you found for me in Seville, which I swore I would never use to kill with?'

'Yes, the sword.' Her eyes upon his face were filled with love, unshadowed and sure of his love for her. 'I'm glad you hung up your sword, *señor hidalgo*, but I wish I'd known you were going to that—that awful day.'

'I didn't know for sure myself, *querida*. It took being without you to bring me to my senses; long days alone, and empty nights when I might have had you in my arms.'

'Now you have me, *señor esposo*.' Arabel held the buckle to the waist of her dress and her smile was just a little wicked. 'Very much where you want me.'

'Not in a stranger's arms, love.'

'In very intimate arms, lover.'

He smiled, and she handed over the *pesetas* for the bull's-head buckle, and they passed on their way to where a boy held his Arab bay in readiness. The time had come for them to go into the hills to the little chapel, to stand in its cool cloister and to know their marriage blessed in every sort of way.

Cortez lifted her to the saddle and climbed up behind her, holding her fast in the crook of his arm.

She felt his lips against her hair and his strong hand against her heart, just above that still tiny emblem of the love they shared, in the sweet hot sun of the south, and in the magic of the Spanish nights.

Best Seller
Romances

Best Seller
Romances

BORN OUT OF LOVE
by Anne Mather

Charlotte had married Matthew Derby eleven years ago, to give her baby a father – after Logan Kennedy had deserted her. Now Matthew was dead, and Charlotte had met Logan again and realised that the past was by no means dead. And that Logan attracted her as much as ever . . .

PASSIONATE INVOLVEMENT
by Lilian Peake

Lucky Tamsin – in Switzerland, spending a long holiday in a luxury hotel, *free* – and with a most attractive man paying her all the attention she wanted! But of course there was a snag – a big one. For she knew that Sarne Brand had completely the wrong ideas about her – and she was not at liberty to tell him the truth. How could the affair end in anything but unhappiness?

STORM OVER MANDARGI
by Margaret Way

Toni had left her job and a go-nowhere romance to join her brother on Mandargi, the cattle station which he managed. She hadn't met the owner, Damon Nyland, but had heard enough about him to determine that she at least wasn't going to fall on the great man's neck when he finally condescended to visit them!

LOVE IN A STRANGER'S ARMS
by Violet Winspear

Arabel had woken up in a hospital in Spain to find she had lost her memory. She knew nothing except what the mysterious Don Cortez Ildefonso de la Dura chose to tell her – and he told her she was his wife! And how could she be sure he was telling the truth?